You Are Stronger Than You Realize

An Extraordinary Cancer Journey to MOTIVATE and INSPIRE YOU to Create the INCREDIBLE LIFE You Were Meant to LIVE

Tanya West

Disclaimer

The content of this book is based on research conducted by the author unless otherwise noted. The information is presented for educational purposes only and is not intended to diagnose or prescribe for any medical or psychological condition, nor to prevent, treat, mitigate, or cure such conditions. The information contained herein is not intended to replace a one-on-one relationship with a doctor or qualified healthcare professional. Therefore, this information is not intended as medical advice, but rather a sharing of knowledge and information based on research and experience. The author encourages you to make your own health care decisions based on your judgment and research in partnership with a qualified healthcare professional. These statements have not been evaluated by the Food and Drug Administration. The information in this book is not intended to diagnose, treat, cure, or prevent any disease.

Please note that everyone is different in terms of allergies. Seek medical advice before trying something new.

Table of Contents

Foreword

I am honoured and blessed to have Tanya West as a trusted friend, confident and uplifting inspirational soul sister. As a fellow multiple cancers survivor, our talks about how strong and resilient a person can be in the face of significant challenges are amazing and real, and yes, *"You Are Stronger Than You Realize!"*

Having emotional, spiritual, energetic, and food-based support sets the stage to launch into overcoming, healing, and thriving for an incredible future. Tanya has tapped into amazing resources that helped her overcome incredible odds and these methods work to help boost the body's focus on healing.

Tanya, I love you for genuinely showing up and having the desire to help others have resources at hand to focus on recovery.

Love you to bits,
Jackie Carmichael Schuurmans
(Your fellow Sista and Fan ♥)

Given that the News of Cancer is scary, and while we each can have our unique paths, who knows where to start? This is a great place!

Preface

I am over the moon excited to be able to share my healing journey with you through the release of my first book.

It has been a long time coming and it's finally here and ready for you! It is time to take on this new opportunity, learn something new and create your new incredible life. I will admit that a book has been in the works for many years and I never finished it because I didn't know how to finish it. I didn't think anyone would want to know **MY** story, so it never got done. I certainly did not expect to go through cancer yet AGAIN! It caught me by surprise and, even though I knew something was wrong with my health, I never thought that it would be as serious as Glioblastoma Stage 4. I thought to myself, *"Where did I go wrong?"*

This wasn't the first time either...

At thirty, I went through Hodgkin's Lymphoma. I felt like the youngest person at the cancer hospital. After finding out, I started learning as much as I could about cancer and why it happens in our bodies. I was given another reason to learn even more quickly because my Mom's breast cancer had also returned.

I spent over 10 years of my life taking health courses and watching documentary series on various health-related topics. I was always interested in healing or preventing cancer from happening in the first place.

Unfortunately, not many people are interested in cancer prevention. They wait until something goes wrong and then they panic and scramble in fear. Imagine what the world would be like if we spent some time and invested money into building up our immune system so we stay healthy?

That would be crazy, right?

I would often think to myself, *"How can I help others?"* This mindset has been the underlying theme for everything I've done in my life. This recent diagnosis made it clear that I still had a few things to learn. Stress management being a big one for me. Oh, glorious stress! Working as an entrepreneur, I was stressed about many things in my life and self-care wasn't at the top of my list. The truth is that, if you are stressed out daily, then eating healthy, using natural products, or taking a million supplements... it doesn't matter.

The stats state that 1 in 2 people will get cancer in their lifetime. I don't know about you but that is scary.

Every single day another person is either diagnosed or given a dire prognosis while in the hospital. Panic and fear are the first feelings that they feel when they hear the words *"You have cancer."* Imagine if, one day, the doctors could share even the tiniest bit of hope with people when giving a diagnosis. The reality is that someone has healed from every type of cancer that is out there and there is always HOPE. Believe it! I wrote this book because I wanted to inspire hope in you and calm any fears that you might be feeling. I want to share with you exactly what's possible.

"Once you choose HOPE, anything's possible."

~ Christopher Reeve

You see, I have been on the other side as well. My Mom had breast cancer before my diagnosis, during my treatment, and after my treatment ended. Every time she was in remission, another lump would come up. When things metastasized to her brain, things started to get pressing. This was my extra incentive to dive more into the holistic world.

We ended up getting radiation at the same time- not your typical mother-daughter bonding experience. I remember going to visit my mom almost daily when she was sick. She couldn't walk anymore and was in bed every time I went to see her. My dad and I kept trying to find ways to help her and watch her slowly deteriorate and lose herself. It was hard to witness and now I understand how being a caregiver can also be heartbreaking.

A few years after losing my mom, a couple of new lumps came up in my chest and I decided to have a preventative double mastectomy, which led to three reconstructions over the years. Having these lumps made hugging someone painful when they would squeeze me close to them. Ouch! I felt like I was in pain all the time. Having to go through getting checked every time a new lump came up wasn't uplifting for me. I didn't want to repeat what my mom's six-year journey and getting radiation on my chest wasn't helping the situation. It increased my odds of getting breast cancer. Please note that this was my decision and I have never regretted it.

Six years later after my mom passed, I lost my dad to heart failure. He also had prostate cancer and had surgery to correct this. After losing him, I was now parentless, became lost, and knew my focus had to change. For a while, I didn't know how to recover from this situation.

I thought about what I wanted to do with my life and what was on my bucket list of things to do. I needed to get my shit together, so I dove into the fitness world to occupy my mind and attempt to heal my heart. I learned a lot from this experience and even more about staying healthy while competing. That is a story for another day.

My background is my WHY- why I feel very passionate about **cancer prevention** and why it is the key to our promising futures.

Now I want to share with you a new story- one of healing your mind, body, and spirit together while also igniting your heart and soul. **You ARE stronger than you realize!** I pray that you will find this book educational, eye-opening, and most importantly, mind-expanding. I think we all could use an inspirational journey that fills our hearts with HOPE.

Remember, at the beginning of this preface, how I mentioned I started writing a book about my cancer journey- the one that never got completed? Well, one night I was lying in bed, and it came to me that this new cancer healing journey **WAS** my book.

There are lots of stories shared from holistic superstars that I have worked with on this journey. It's like each person that came into my life was an integral piece of the healing puzzle- that without one of those pieces, it never would have got completed. I am very, very thankful.

I hope you find this book useful and, even if you don't understand all the topics, that's okay. If you get even one takeaway that will improve your future, that is enough for me. I want to make a difference in your life and see you smile about your incredible future- one that YOU can create yourself. Remember, all you have to be is open to new possibilities. There are always more options for you to try. Keep going and keep believing in **YOUR POWER.**

With love, Tanya xo

I want to inspire you. I want you to look at me and say,
"Because of you, I NEVER gave up HOPE."

~ Unknown

Acknowledgements

I am grateful to have had so many people help me along the way. This book is a collaboration of many transformational people that have supported me throughout this incredibly emotional adventure. They offered their time to me and, without having all of them, there would be missing pieces of this story.

Special thanks to my friends and family for listening to me through this whole experience. You visited me after brain surgery, listened to my anxiety and my panic attacks at any hour in the day, including in the middle of the night, started a GoFundMe fundraiser while I was recovering in the hospital to support me financially, sent me messages of love several times a day, including daily Snapchat videos of a six-year-old couch fort building expert, drew pictures for me to hang in the hospital or place on my fridge, and reminded me of how special, worthy, beautiful, and deserving of kindness I am, no matter what – hair or no hair.

Thank you to St. Andrew's United Church. Even though I haven't been there since my parents passed, it is nice to be remembered. Your prayers, cards, and warm messages are much appreciated.

An extra special thanks to Integrity Seminars, whose community has truly changed my life. I don't think I would be here today if it were not for your compassion, kindness, and love. Thank you for holding a group Zoom call and praying for me while undergoing an emergency Craniotomy. That brought so much joy and tears to my eyes. Your thoughts and prayers were heard and answered. Your big-hearted community of amazingly exceptional people has impacted me in ways I can't even begin to put into words.

Thank you.

Thank you, Deanna C Photography for my cover and author photos.

With love, Tanya xo

My Cancer Story -
Where the Journey Began

Imagine this for a moment...

You get a call from your doctor telling you that cancer is no longer growing within your body! This waiting to exhale, extremely emotional moment, created heart-expanding, unbelievable gratitude inside of me! This truly was the best day of my life! Tears welled up within my eyes and began to stream down my face as I broke down with happiness. Feelings of pure joy washed over me and I am thankful to be alive.

My name is Tanya West, and, on October 2nd, 2020, I was diagnosed with Stage 4 Glioblastoma. It turned my world upside down. I thought I was dreaming- surely, they had made a mistake and got my records wrong. I knew I hadn't been feeling well, was getting too many headaches, and was very tired. I noticed a little extra pressure on the left side of my head and that turned out to be where the tumour was located. Yet, no one seemed to have any answers for me, and I never thought that it would be cancer-

Again...WTF?

How could this be happening in my life?

WHY?

I'd already been through cancer three times and never wanted it to happen again and NOW? This time, a neurosurgeon was telling me that it was incurable.
Incurable...

Are you kidding me?

You can imagine the mental impact those words had on me. At that moment, a part of my soul died instantly. I felt there was absolutely NO HOPE and was overcome with tears of sadness.

What am I going to do?

Please may this not be real.

Talk about a soul-crushing moment in your life. I never want anyone to feel this way. Having NO hope is not a great feeling to carry.
The last time I had gone through cancer, I was thirty and had Hodgkin's Lymphoma. I made it through and survived six months of Chemotherapy and seventeen days of radiation on my chest.
I was sick for several years before this was discovered. Yes, years!
I had night sweats, extreme fatigue, and itchy skin that would not go away! Several doctors, naturopaths, and even a dermatologist could not figure this out. I mean who thinks a twenty something-year-old would get cancer?
When it got to the point where I could barely breathe, my chiropractor discovered I had no air going into my left lung. He said, "*I think you should go to the emergency and ask for an*

x-ray." He was right – there they discovered a large mass in my chest that shouldn't have been there... and so began that roller coaster of a journey.

When I was nearly done with my chemotherapy IV treatments, my mom told me her breast cancer had returned and, a year later, she passed away. Losing my parents, having a preventative double mastectomy with three reconstructions, and being told all the horrible things that could happen to me with this new cancer– brain cancer of all things– was all very serious, and it was not what I had pictured for my life!!!

I got home from the hospital and had many sleepless nights. I thought about why this kept happening to me. I wondered, *"Why do I KEEP going through cancer this many times*?" I had to figure this out and see what I had left in my dustpan that was cluttering up my mind.

This time, I knew I had to wake up and pay attention. I wanted to help people so if not now, then when? What was I waiting for? There was no way I was going to let this happen and leave an untold story inside me... not happening!

Over the next few weeks, I had developed high anxiety as I was trying to understand how I could help myself get better. I had to find myself because I never wanted to go through this **EVER** again. At this moment, I knew I had to dive into my mind for answers and it was going to be a deep emotional dive. Thankfully, I wouldn't be making this journey alone.

This might make you laugh– I found it almost a cruel joke from the Universe to have had a tumour on the emotional center of my brain. "Very funny," I thought as I looked up to the sky. I have had several laugh-out-loud moments saying, "You have got to be kidding me!"

Growing up, I was known as the shy kid. I didn't talk about my feelings, and I didn't talk much at all. I had issues fully letting people know how I felt and sharing my emotions, especially when someone hurt me or made me feel embarrassed. I would bottle that shit up and keep it inside.

Pop! I put that cork back on that bottle and didn't deal with that on that day. No thank you!

I mean, talk about my emotions? Who does that?

Step one of this new healing journey, was me learning how to express myself, no matter what I was feeling inside. No more stuffing those emotions down into the bottom of the bottle. I had to let my emotions out.

I often would say, *"Could you have not picked something a little less serious?"* while shaking my fist in the air. During this healing experience, I have to say that, if it hadn't been so serious, I may not have made the changes in my life that helped me create my incredible future and changed my life forever.

"Life doesn't happen to you; it happens for you."

~ Tony Robbins

It's been a work-in-progress- that's for sure. Talking about how I feel and asking for help are two very tough things for me. Some say it's a quality of a "Type C personality", which seems to attract cancer to our bodies- more on that topic later in this book. All I can say is that I've learned much these past few months and I have many people that have touched my life in such a positive way. They made me change the way I saw my future and how I could help others do the same.

A fire was lit inside me that I cannot wait to share with YOU. This is the reason why I'm sharing this book- I feel this information is transformative and it has truly changed my life for the better.

This is the book I wish I was handed right after my surgery. Being told you have cancer and then given a book to help guide you through this process would have helped.

This book is even valuable for anyone going through any dis-ease and wanting to reframe their mindset and create a brighter, more positive future. If I can heal my body, I know you can too!

I recommend getting a motivational journal to use while reading this book and writing down your thoughts on the Action Steps at the end of each chapter. This helps you to lock in the intentions needed to make some changes and find the JOY within you.

There are two sides to this healing journey: the western medicine side and the holistic side. The medical side, who puts the fear of God into you, and the holistic side, where there are many options that you can explore. Why put all your eggs in one basket when you can do more yourself? All you have to do is open your mind and believe in what's possible.

Each person who wrote in this book shares in their own style. Some will resonate more with you than others and that is okay. It is your choice, and it is your life. You are the one that knows what will work for **YOU** and what will not. Making our own decisions... isn't that a wonderful idea!

In this book, we are going to work through the **4 Principles of Healing, called M.I.N.D.** That is really where this journey all begins.

M **Mindset and Medicine**
I   **Increase Your Immune System and Strengthen Your Body**
N **No More Dirt! Detoxify Your Life and Heal Your Spirit**
D **Discover Your Destiny by Raising Your Vibrations**

Action Step:

Use the "I Am Stronger Than You Realize" Journal or one that motivates you—unless you have an addiction to them like me and you have a collection ready to go.

"My mission in life is to lead, motivate and inspire myself and others to shine bright and live a healthy life with purpose."

~ Tanya West

Best Day of My Life

Let's go back to that most incredible moment...

It was April 19th, 2021, and my Oncologist gave me a call earlier than expected. He shared some amazing news— that there was no more cancer growing inside my body!

No more cancer!

I was stable and was healing where I needed to heal.

As the tears ran down my face, I was overwhelmed with joy and gratitude. With a huge smile upon my face, I looked up and said, "Thank you! Thank you!"

After I caught my breath and wiped my face, I called my friends and my family to share the good news with them because this was a fantastic life-changing day— the best day of my life! It was a day that will forever be imprinted in my mind.

I wanted to share this experience with you because you can have this same feeling and feel this way on any given day and hopefully without going through any dis-ease.

When you think about how happy you **CAN** be in your life today, I want you to close your eyes and picture hearing words that would set your soul on fire. Let a smile grow on your face and feel that weight lift off your shoulders. Doesn't that feel good?

What if you could avoid cancer altogether and still feel blissful like this? No one needs to wait for something sad to happen to them to experience this feeling. I can tell you right now that **YOU** can create this any time, any day of the week without going through cancer four times.

Please note that not all scans will come back with great results. Some scans might not or you may have to wait in mystery not knowing and this can be scary. I've had those scans too. It is really challenging and frustrating to stay and wait to hear from the doctor.

It's also okay to not be okay.

Do your best to not sit and stay in fear though. I've waited three weeks to hear back from the doctor and this was for something serious. Occupy yourself, find something to do and keep moving forward. Feel free to also use your voice. You are not just a patient number – you are also a human being.

Action Step:

Celebrate every good moment that happens in your life, no matter how big or how small. Reward yourself in some way. The more you let the Universe know how grateful you are for even the littlest things; the more positive things will happen in your life. Make a list of what you are grateful for and keep adding to it. This is a great list to review when you have some down days. **Read it and see the POWER it has for you.**

"After watching your video sharing the news, picture me there with you jumping up and down with joy! I am so happy for you!"

~ Vicki

Principle of Healing I

Mindset and Medical

How Does Medicine Fit Into Our Lives?

Can We Do Only One or Are There More Options for Us to Choose From?

Moving Forward –
Your Thought Processes

"80% of your success is mindset."

~ Marisa Peer

If you have been recently diagnosed with a dis-ease, allow yourself to take the time you need to go through the emotions you're feeling. If you want to cry, then cry. If you're angry, be angry. If you want to throw something across the room, do it. Don't throw this book though, okay? When you're ready to come back and move forward, I'll be here waiting for you. I've got your back!

I know that, if you're not in the right mindset at this moment, then anything you read will just go in one ear and out the other because you're not in the present moment. This is one of the most important chapters in the book because it's going to put your mindset in the right place, helping you to move forward and start healing your body.

Let me put this here for you ♥ ♥ ♥ so you can find your place.

The mind is a POWERFUL thing and listens all too closely. I have learned that I don't need to tell my body that it HAS cancer. Why keep reminding it? I don't need anybody else reminding me either because this is distracting and takes me away from my focus on healing.

I started to LOVE myself and every part of me completely– body, mind, and spirit. I don't even want to be "fighting" cancer. This seems to be the most common encouragement, *"Keep fighting a good fight!"*, *"You are such a fighter!"*, *"A true warrior!"*. Being a warrior is kind of cool, however, I don't want to be fighting with anything, especially not my own body. I love my body!

I am not exactly sure how you are feeling today, however loving yourself for everything that you are sounds much better to me in any situation. What do you think?

Your mind hears your words, whether they are harsh or good. Trust me when I say it is listening. We can be so hard on ourselves without even realizing it. Words do matter. Think about yesterday... how many times did you say something that was not so kind about yourself or anyone else? I remember being told that, if you wouldn't say those words to your younger self, then maybe you shouldn't be saying them or thinking them about anyone else.

I might sound like your mom here but be kind to yourself and to others. See the change you can make with those around you by showing KINDNESS. Love and gratitude are the strongest vibrations in the world and that is what we want to feel in our bodies. It creates a physical change within us that leaves a smile on our face and people feel this from us. This feeling is true happiness that can radiate from us in every direction. Just like negative emotions impact us, we impact ourselves and others with positive ones.

I can't even tell you how many people came up to me months after my initial diagnosis and told me I even sounded different and, to be honest, I felt it!

"6 minutes of a negative emotion can suppress the immune system for 21 hours."
~ Berk 2001.

How do you want to feel daily? Do you want to stay in a state of fear, thinking "what if?" or "if only I had?" Fear and faith cannot occupy the same place at the same time. I would rather feel faith than being stuck in a place of fear. I spent way too much of my life worried about all the things that can go wrong. Now, I'm changing my mindset into a more positive one.

I know this can be challenging and I'm still working at it every single day.

I know that it will get easier. I promise you that it will.

Our brains are naturally set to worry about what could go wrong. When you are given ten compliments and one of them is a bad one, which one are you going to focus on? The bad one, right? I know this can be frustrating. This behaviour was learned from our caveman days. If there was a saber tooth tiger outside of the cave, they needed to be ready for all the possibilities of what could go horribly wrong. Let's face it– we are long past that caveman age and can learn to rewire our brains to a more positive mindset.

I'd rather experience JOY every single day of my life! I have spent too much time trying to find it. I would say to myself, "*I need more happiness in my life. Where can I find more of this good feeling?*" Feeling that my life was being lived without joy made me unhappy. I would be so hard on myself and wondered what I was working towards in my life. I thought cruel things about myself and said a lot of things that I didn't mean. Regretfully, I can remember them all too well because... my mind heard me.

One day, I realized that this feeling of joy and happiness had to come from within ME. No matter what my circumstances were or what was going on in my life, where I was living, or the people around me, joy was something that I was learning I had to create. From playing with Legos, putting together colour-changing 3D puzzles, or even visualizing the creation of this book sparked joy within me. All the fun that went into creating what the book cover would look like and even the back of the book sparked more joy. I thought, "What would I say and how could I make it sound inspiring?" I visualized all the bits and pieces that would put it together and make it become a real reality. I let go of the "one day I'll do that book," which is what I wrote on my whiteboard admittedly all too many years ago. I was giving myself HOPE.

I promised myself that, no matter what, I would create more joyful days. I would wake up in the morning and my first thought, even though sometimes I was very tired, was to repeatedly visualize my future and what it would look like until it put a smile on my face. I would do the same exercise before I fell asleep at night. I'd lay in bed and think of my future and how amazing it was going to be. I could not wait to see it all unfold. It felt like a flame ignited within me and was ready to burst out of my chest. I could barely contain myself! Have you ever felt this way? It feels so amazing inside.

Even think about the clothing that you're wearing. Whether you realize it or not, if you're wearing a shirt that has violence depicted on it, or something most people would consider to be evil, this can also affect how you feel inside. You may want to consider giving it away or getting rid of some shirts because they ARE affecting your mood.

We can create our futures by doing this incredible mental exercise. Set your mindset and dial into positivity more and more every day. It may take you some time, keep going! Every time you think something negative, catch yourself and replace it with something positive. It will get easier. It is worth noting too that our subconscious mind does not register don'ts or negatives etc. When I say *"don't think about a green turtle,"* I bet you did! Focus on the positive side when saying your positive affirmations. Also, feel free to still vent when something happens and then let it go – instead of repeating it over and over in your head. Good things will start to arrive in your life. I promise you.

Finally, remember that dis-ease does not heal overnight. I won't make any promises to you on this point.

Your body is not my body.

Our goal here is to work on your path to healing. Deal? You have to believe you can do it and keep believing that every day. Your subconscious mind will start to listen to you. You have to do something better.

If you believe you CAN, you will!
If you believe you CAN'T, you won't!
Work hard.
Create new habits.
Make praising yourself familiar.

When you walk by a mirror and your reflection catches your eye, take a moment to say "*Hey, I love you, you know!*"

Choose to fully LIVE. It is your choice.

Action Step:

What brings you Joy? How can you create more Joy in your life? Make a list of 5 things in your journal and start to enjoy life a little bit more every day.

Me, Myself, and Irene?

"Take care of your body, it's the only place you have to live."

~ Jim Rohn

Have you seen this movie? It is very funny. Laugh as much as possible throughout this entire journey as it is the best medicine for your spirit. It feels good and is super healthy for you and bringing you up into a higher vibration.

You might think I'm crazy for saying this and that's okay. On this journey, I started out separating myself from my brain, body, and spirit.

You are not your body.
You are not your brain, and you are not your spirit.
You are You! That bright shining soul that is 100% you!

You are the person created from the experiences in your life and from the people that were around you, be they good or bad. At this point in your life, you can choose to keep going down the same path, if it is good, or choose a different one. The choice is yours. The amazing thing about life is that it is what you make it to be. **YOU are the author of your own story.** So, what are you going to write?

"The definition of insanity is doing the same thing over and over again and expecting different results."

~ Albert Einstein

I know it might sound weird, but depending on the situation, I do talk to my body, brain, and spirit. I would say, "I love you, body!" Then I would give my shoulder or my hand a kiss. Hey! During COVID, you have to love yourself.

I want my body to know I love it!

I also want my brain to know that we're healing every day, creating new healthy cells in our body in every way.

I would remind my spirit that I had faith and hope that things were going to be okay. I would hug myself and say, "We're going to be okay, everybody! I promise you are safe, and we've got this!" In later chapters, when I say "we" I might be referring to me, myself, and Tanya (or insert your name here).

I'm not bananas, I swear! (Insert big smiley face)

Action Step:

Talk to your body out loud and let it know how much you love it every day. You can even write down a list of things that you love about it. Let's face it- you are awesome!

Trusting Yourself and Believing It

"What if I fail? Oh but my darling, what if you fly?"

~ Erin Hanson

Trust- now **THIS** is an interesting topic. Why don't we trust ourselves? I know I've had a hard time trusting myself and my abilities in my business and life. I had doubts about what I could do and if I COULD truly believe in myself. I thought that Trust was about trusting other people and the reality was I simply didn't trust myself. I will admit that I haven't always made the best choices, especially with relationships.

One night, I dreamt about my mom. When I was young, she trusted me to paint a new design on my brother's old bedroom walls. I may be aging myself here, but we rag rolled the top and the bottom together and I ended up creating a stencil of a rose for the border. At that time, I was pretty good at stencilling and painting roses. I had that down pat and I enjoyed painting, too. Back then, my Mom trusted me with this task and I did it, so why was I now having a hard time trusting myself at this stage in my life.

In that same dream, my dad trusted me to be a good goalie on our soccer team. He was my coach and I have to say that, coming from him, this was a big act of trust. Playing soccer was one of the best things in my life and my dad loved soccer so much. When he was a young adult, he

39

was an amazing soccer player and truly had a passion for this game. I remember seeing a few newspaper clippings about his successes. So, I thought to myself, "If my parents could trust me when I was younger, why was I having trouble trusting myself now?" As an adult, it was time to let go of my doubts and believe in myself. I had to TRUST myself. If I could do that, I can get through anything.

Anything is possible for anyone, within reason. I'm staying in the present moment as that is what is working best for me. When asked how I am doing, I say, "I'm healing every day in every way. Stronger and stronger every day." Thank you, Mom and Dad, for trusting in me. Now, it is time for me to believe in myself and let any doubt I had in my abilities GO! Thank you, Mom and Dad, you are missed.

P.S. Waiting for my superpowers to kick in!

Placing Your Trust in Others

In any situation in your life, there will be many people involved in it. During the hard times, some people will step up and some will step back. When in a crisis, expect this to happen and know that some of the people will make promises to you and not follow through. This is not about you; it is about them and what is going on in their life. Don't take it personally! Instead, know and be thankful for those who do rise in a big exceptional way. I am very thankful for all the people who have offered their services and kindness to me, and I will forever be grateful for their impact on my life.

Action Step:

In your journal, make a list of ways others have trusted you. Then, make a list of ways you have trusted yourself. Both will be great lists to remind you how amazing you are. You got this. I believe in you! **Trust yourself.**

Trust = Surrender

Another point I wanted to make about trust is that, when you surrender to the Universe or a higher power or to God whatever it is that you believe, that magical force that makes both positive or negative things happen for you is "out there." The true definition of manifestation is that, when in a high vibration, visualize and truly feel the feelings you would if this were to come true, then let it go and it will happen for you. If you believe in yourself and your abilities 100%, manifestation will happen... just let go.

While out for a drive one day, I had an interesting thought. I needed to get groceries and there is one long street to get to the good grocery store down the road. I started to think, "What if I can get green lights all the way through to the store?" I believed I could, held on to that belief, and then doubt slowly crept in. I thought, "Oh! I don't know if I can make it to this light," and sure enough, I suddenly started to get red lights again. It dawned on me that, to get more green lights, I had to let go and believe that it was possible and surrender to a higher power that would help me manifest my true desires. Now, this can work for things bigger than green lights! I noticed my manifestation skills kept improving daily. It could be winning an Amazon gift card in a course or winning a designer bag in a draw. Start to listen more to that inner voice inside our heads called intuition.

I find that, when you listen to that soft voice, you will see more good things happen in your life. Often, this voice is the one you usually would ignore, but understand that it's the one voice you should be listening to more often.

Another example would be the day when I was looking to update my website with some accomplishments that I had done. As I was flipping through my Instagram to see what I had done in my life, I came across a post where I had shared a picture of a Wonder Woman glass. It wasn't my glass, but I had shared it from someone else's post. I think it was from another fitness person's page that was using the same pre-workout that I was at the time.

Later that day, it popped into my head that maybe I should just look and see if that Wonder Woman glass was on a Facebook buy and sell group. Guess what? I found it! Someone happened to be selling it and I purchased it right away. What are the coincidences that happened at that moment? I found that, if you just surrender or listen to that voice, it's amazing how strong you will be once you turn up your intuition dial. This will cause you to listen to that voice more often.

Turning up my intuition, trusting myself, and creating more moments or opportunities is truly a magical thing. The key here is to trust that the Universe will work for you. If you put a thought and an intention out there, it will happen. You just have to believe that it will, let it go, and surrender.

Action Step:

Let's have some fun with this! What is one little thing that you want in your life? Remember: this has to be something that you want for yourself and not controlling anybody else because it doesn't work that way. For example, it could be someone buying you a free coffee or tea that day at some point. Set your intention, let it go, and see what happens.

Setting Intentions

"Our intention creates our reality."

~ Wayne Dyer

Creating an intention for your day can make a big impact on it and your future. I wake up every day and tell myself it is going to be a great day and, you know what, it is! I knew what my future was going to look like. I set my thoughts on it, and even created a digital vision board for my computer. Along with my book mock-up, I put meeting someone who is kind to me and loves me just how I am having a wellness retreat in Arizona and skipping these traditional cold Canadian Winters on there. Brrrr! It also included reminders to love myself every day, be brave, and keep believing in my own capabilities.

One day, you might find that you won't need to create a vision board anymore. Your skills to create the life that you want will naturally start to happen because your intention setting has become stronger than ever in your entire life. You will be vibrating at a higher frequency and start to attract more good things TO you. When you figure out how it's done, you will think that it's a magical thing, and I will share more with you on this in a later chapter.

Try this for yourself. Love yourself. I've said it before- the power of the mind is a beautiful thing!

Action Step:

Wake up tomorrow and say out loud- yes, out loud- that today is going to be an incredible day! See what happens. Get your own digital vision board template for free on my website and see what your mind will create for YOU. You are the one who decides what WILL happen. See it! Feel it! Believe it!

What to Say When You Don't Know What to Say

"Too often we underestimate the power of a touch, a smile, a kind word, a listening ear, an honest compliment, or the smallest act of caring, all of which have the potential to turn a life around."

~ Leo Buscaglia

I remember that, when I was rushed into the hospital and ended up having emergency brain surgery, it was a fearful time. Not that I remember much of it. Many people reached out to me after an emotional quick video I had done. To this day, I still haven't read those initial comments on that post, but as the journey continued, I do remember... some of the comments people made.

When someone is diagnosed, their need for support doesn't end the next day. They need support for the entire journey, which is more than just a week or a month. Let's face it– we ALL know someone who has gone through cancer and not all have happy endings. If you have a positive result with the same cancer as I was diagnosed with, as in, they are still alive and doing well, I am all for hearing more about it.

I chose NOT to say that I have something. I chose to love my body and say "for any cancer cells that may or may not be there..." I do believe my body hears me and has heard me say things in my head that may not have been so nurturing.

45

Here are some tips on what is helpful to say to someone:

- I'm sorry this has happened to you.
- If you ever feel like talking, I'm here to listen.
- How can I help you?
- I care about you.
- I'm thinking about you.

Here are some that are not helpful:

- I know just how you feel. Do you?
- I know someone who had cancer. Almost everyone does these days- no unhappy endings please! That is not motivating!
- I'm sure you'll be fine. Get better soon. -No pressure here.
- Don't worry, keep up the good fight!
- How long did the doctor say you have? UGH...seriously.

Bottom line: **BE KIND**.

I spent a lot of time trying to figure out why this happened in my life. I'm learning to forgive and accept what has happened in the past and, what I didn't realize was, I had been carrying it ALL this time. It took months of learning and understanding to rewire my brain and mindset.

When someone's going through a dis-ease, they're scared, they're frightened, and fear is the first thing they're usually going to feel when given a diagnosis. They yearn for kind words, kind people, and happy stories that end on a positive note. Make them smile, offer to help, cook them a meal- there's always something you can do, even if it's simply saying, "I'm thinking of you."

My friend Danielle and I started sending each other notes and cards in the mail. I have received so many nice cards from people I don't even know. A little bit of love goes a long way. Give it a try. They will appreciate it and it will make them smile. It will be something that brightens what could have been a gloomy day for them. It is nice to get something in the mail that isn't a bill!

Supporting someone going through a difficult time means everything to that person, especially during COVID-19 when it's harder to get hugs and love from those that you care about. I've had to learn how to love myself, hug myself, and show myself daily how much I love me! I know it isn't easy to do this every day. Find a way that's comfortable for you to know that you are loved and... believe it!

By the way, the right way to hug yourself is to place your right hand under your left armpit and then your left hand on your right shoulder. Give yourself a good squeeze and tell yourself how much you love you!

Sometimes I would look out my window and see the people walking by without any care in the world. I felt so alone, like no one else was on this challenging journey. While you're inside looking out, watching as they go by, they don't know that you're in there not feeling well, having a hard time even making yourself a meal. Not having enough energy to get off the couch. You wish you could be like them and take a time out from your life, be normal, and not have to face the things that you're dealing with now. I remember thinking that, one day, I would feel like that again— without any care in the world.

My sister-in-law and I were going to see the neurosurgeon for a follow-up appointment, all the hospital windows were filled with beautiful yellow hearts with messages of HOPE written on them for those walking by to read and smile. A friend of mine had done a reading on me a few weeks earlier and she mentioned that she kept seeing

47

buttercups and this didn't have any meaning to me at the time- until this day.

There were hundreds of hearts along the wall and my sister-in-law stopped and said, "Hey! Look at this one!" This is what it said, "Cheer up buttercup, you have people that love you no matter what."

On came the waterworks.

I want to take a moment to say thank you to those who helped me with meals. It meant so much to me, especially during chemotherapy. It's the little things that make all the difference in the world. The more LOVE, the better.

Action Step:

Reach out to someone you know who could use a nice compliment. See how it feels to make someone's day a little brighter. Share in your journal what happened and how it made you feel.

Type "C" Personality

"Be the type of person you want to meet."

~ Mahantesh Biradar

The Cancer-Prone Personality. ~ Temoshok 1987

"Cancer has been correlated with non-assertiveness, the inability to express emotion, and hopelessness. Depression is the emotion reputedly linked to cancer incidence...and such findings have been published in the Journal of American Medical Association." ~ Mind as Healer, p. xli

I mentioned earlier about explaining this "type" further. If you have a very giving personality where you give, give, and give, to help others before yourself, never take time for yourself, and take on too much, over time this will affect your body... and not in a good way.

People pleasers.

Repressing emotions such as anger.

Type "C" personalities have a hard time expressing their feelings when managing stress. They will bottle it up and this can lead to dis-ease within the body. I'm raising my hand up in the air. That is 100% me.

Although there is contradictory evidence out there on this topic, I found this to be true about my personality before I was diagnosed. Doing anything to make other people happy made me nervous because I wouldn't want anyone in my life to be upset with me. I would give up everything else in my life and ultimately lose myself. I don't think I even knew WHO I was! Over the last six years, working on myself and becoming more aware of who I am changed me. I've taken lots of personal development courses and they had a big impact on my life. Personal development is a lifelong journey and I realize how much I have learned already.

How about you? What type of personality are you? Do you have an easy or hard time expressing your emotions? I can tell you right now– get that bottled-up emotional shit out of you! You will feel so much better!

Visualize all the unsaid thoughts and emotions you haven't expressed to anyone that continue to build up inside you. From the soles of your feet to the top of your head, they want to overflow but can't because they are stuck in your body with nowhere to go– that isn't good! Your body will feel this and react badly to it. It is your choice. If there is one thing I know, it is that your body will feel healthier after letting those emotions fly free.

When in doubt, let it out.

Action Step:

What are your thoughts on this topic? Think about the people you know who have been diagnosed. Does it hold true?

Radiation Treatment – How to Keep Calm

*"Keep calm and stay **strong**."*

(Finish this with the power word that gives you strength)

Willingly getting radiation was a scary thing for me. As I mentioned earlier, my mom went through breast cancer on and off for over six years before it metastasized to her brain. I had to watch as she went through getting radiation on her head, witnessing what it did to her mentally.

She lost herself.

Suddenly, I was faced with the same treatment– having radiation on my head. I remember freaking out in the hospital when I was told that I would need to go through radiation. Fear ensued at the thought of this. I thought, *"Oh no, please no. I didn't want to go through this. Anything but this*!" My greatest fear was losing myself as my mom did.

The doctors assured me that times had changed, and they were now using a more localized form of radiation that would only target the area where the cancer was and avoiding "at best" the healthy cells. Although they couldn't assure me that some healthy cells might get damaged during this process, I was promised that I wouldn't deteriorate away as my mom had.

The owner at Integrity Seminars contacted me and told me that there was a hypnotic therapy that she had used on

51

someone else, and the doctors couldn't believe how well she made it through radiation. So, I figured I might as well try it and see what would happen.

Every day during radiation, I listened to it on my iPod. Sometimes, I wouldn't hear the whole thing as I would fall asleep listening to it, but it would continue to play. I knew that, by listening to this hypnosis through this treatment, I was doing something beneficial for my body and my mind It was assuring my subconscious mind that everything was going to be okay. I was going to be okay, and I started to believe it.

The next step was figuring out how much medication I needed to take to keep me calm during the actual radiation. On Day One, I took one Ativan before the radiation, and I was so nervous. It felt like the ten-minute radiation took thirty minutes and I came out of there very much out of breath. Going through four weeks of this? That was not happening!

On the second day, I increased my Ativan and took it sooner than I had the day before. Again, my mind got the better of me and this resulted in me coming out of the radiation lost for breath and having a panic attack in my sister in law's truck. I thought, *"Okay, maybe I need a little more than medication?"*

I talked to the psychosocial department the next day and she gave me some good tips for getting through the next treatment. I found a nice relaxing ocean sounds meditation that would keep me calm if I let that play. My radiation toolkit ended up being 2 Ativan, my meditation music, a pink rose quartz heart crystal, a little tiger my nephew got me, and a blanket to keep me warm. Remember how this was when you were a kid- all cozy and safe snug as a bug in a rug?

I did try letting my mind go somewhere else, whether it was at a beach or somewhere that was relaxing for me;

however, I couldn't focus on this as it was making me more nervous about what was going on.

My best method was to remember how many times they were turning me in the machine, so I knew how many more minutes were left based on where I was positioned. I had to be present as much as I didn't want to be. Radiation got easier every day and I was STILL very thankful when the four weeks were finally DONE!

After my last radiation treatment, my sister-in-law greeted me with a necklace of bells, and I happily rang the Bell of Hope, signalling that this part had finally been completed. After I went outside and was about to get into her truck, I stopped, took a moment to breathe, and did a little dance, celebrating how I was so thankful to have gotten through that process. Hallelujah!

Action Step:

If you have to have this done, do whatever works for YOU and keeps you calm. Use your voice. What worked for me may or may not work for you. **Again, trust yourself.**

Hypnotherapy
Rae-ann Wood-Schatz

"Takes a village to raise a child, takes a tribe to kill cancer."

~ Rae-ann Wood-Schatz

"You are completely relaxed...you feel warm and comfortable...you feel you really need to close your eyes and sleep...your eyelids are getting heavy...heavier...and heavier...slowly, you close them...now they are closed...you are getting sleepier...and sleepier...you are going to SLEEP... deeper and deeper asleep...SLEEP!"

Many of us are familiar with this scene: A bizarre-looking man holds a clock pendant and continuously, determinedly swings it in front of a vulnerable, lost-looking young woman. He utters the phrase repeatedly, in slower and lower intonation: *"You're getting sleepy... You're getting sleepy..."* The girl stares blankly into the clock. The world turns and swirls around her, spiralling and spiralling. Then eventually, she starts to act like (a) a zombie, (b) a vamp, (c) a chicken, or (d) all the above simultaneously.

Thanks to popular culture, hypnotism has achieved an eerie, mystical, otherworldly, and sometimes mysterious or magical reputation. While the scenario illustrated above may have a little ring of truth to it- hypnosis using verbal suggestion is powerful and people under hypnosis can be made to believe and therefore act, as a different identity-

55

there is certainly a lot more to hypnotism than meets the eye.

Doubtless one of the most intriguing – yet also one of the most bewildering – topics known to man, hypnotism transcends boundaries as it continues to be studied, analyzed, and interpreted in diverse fields of wisdom. From medicine, psychology, new age, self-help, religion, history, media, and popular culture, hypnotism is given different meanings, interpretations, and uses with the conclusions never being final and the reports ever evolving.

This may be rooted in one thesis– that studying hypnotism would inevitably mean studying the human mind, and the human mind is an ever-changing overlapping Universe of significance, interpretation, and purpose.

In this chapter, we will touch on the different aspects of understanding hypnotism and how it was and still is being utilized, or condemned by some parties, for various reasons. Read on and judge for yourself. Join me as we try to discuss some of the major points of view regarding mind control. Explore – or reject – the possibility of controlling the human mind and the life of the person possessing it.

Hypnosis: Fact or Fraud?

"The Sleeping Prophet" Edgar Cayce would command himself to engage in out-of-body and near-death experiences through self-hypnosis. Under a trance state, he would give readings and diagnoses to people he had never met. His followers documented almost 14,000 journeys into the spirit realm made through his subconscious mind – or what Cayce referred to as the soul.

Sensational historian David Lewis revealed that Adolf Hitler was once hypnotized, and this may have been the root of the kind of life he led. Lewis claimed that, in 1918, Hitler believed he had gone completely blind despite diagnoses of doctors who said nothing was wrong with his eyes. Through hypnosis, a doctor suggested to Hitler that indeed, he had lost his eyesight, but through willpower, he could make himself see again.

"That's because God made him an exceptional person," the good doctor added. "Since then," Lewis said, "the hypnosis marked Hitler so much that he took to life believing he was exceptional, and the rest, as they say, is history."

Have you read about clairvoyants reaching into other dimensions to get rare or secret information? How about mediums meddling with the underworld and calling the dead? Hypnosis stories – are they for real?

Hypnosis may be one of the most debated and controversial topics known to us, but that doesn't mean we can't get our facts right. Before we delve further into our study of mind control and its twists and turns, let's try to get our facts straight first. Here are some of the most popular – **yet unproven** – takes on hypnosis.

The Powerful Mystical Mysterious Master Hypnotist

No, he doesn't have supernatural powers.

She's not casting an ancient spell.

He's not an apostle of Satan.

Neither is she a saint.

Your friendly neighbourhood hypnotist – be she a licensed doctor or a new-age practitioner – does not possess that special kind of "animal magnetism" either. That was dismissed as early as the 17th century. Today, it is proven that, to be able to initiate a hypnosis session, the hypnotist may merely provide a very specific visual element to focus on such as soothing music and a very convincing, authoritative spiel repeated in a monotone. You need only to be relaxed, aware, and willing to be hypnotized. Of course, the effects of hypnosis rely on the hypnotist's ability and experience as well as the motivation and mental conditioning of the subject.

The Dreamer

People who claim to be under hypnosis – are they dreaming? The opposite is true. When you are under hypnosis, you are more alert than normal. Being under hypnotism requires your mind to focus intensely, whether it's on the swinging motion of the pendulum clock, the monotone pattern of the hypnotist's voice, or on the sound of your breathing as you relax. For your subconscious to take over, you need to concentrate intently. Under a state of trance, you will still be fully aware of the things you will be saying and doing as suggested by the hypnotist, including activities not related to sleeping such as walking, running around, reading, laughing, and even acting like a chicken.

The Live Chicken Eating Girl

No way... Not eating live chicken– unless of course, it's something you have wanted to experience. It was widely believed that hypnotists can turn people into zombie-like, robotic creatures ready to obey their master's beck and call. Popular culture portrayed hypnotized people to either behave differently or commit extraordinary, life-threatening, illegal, or immoral acts.

Sorry to disappoint you and your cinematic notions, but hypnotism cannot force you to do things against your will unless the hypnotist is pointing a gun at you. You, an ordinary, law-abiding citizen, will not turn wild and go out trashing people's windshields when under hypnosis. You will still maintain your principles. Even if instructed, you won't trample upon your religion's holiest shrine. Your sense of right and wrong will remain intact. Nobody can make you strip in front of a crowd unless you want to.

The hypnotist can only make suggestions that can alter your consciousness, making you more open and likely to accept the new possibility that is being offered. People who have experienced stage hypnotism have said they can refuse to follow the hypnotist's suggestions, but that "it's easier to follow him." This is so because the active, aggressive, decision-making part of the consciousness becomes timid when under a trance. So, it is "easier" to automatically respond to suggestions.

To some extent, the hypnotist can deeply influence the actions and the way his subjects behave. Conversely, the effect of hypnosis also depends upon your motivation, willingness, and faith to make it work for you.

Suffice it to say, the myth of "the control of a human lies with the hypnotist" is fundamentally not true and, at the end of the day, the ability to leverage the power of hypnosis was, always, and will remain in the domain of the person accessing it as a tool.

The All-Around Wonder Solution

On the other side of the spectrum, some people perceive hypnosis as dark and manipulative while others have prescribed it as a cure-all for all kinds of conditions from weight loss to finding the "key" to financial success. Hypnotists claim they can help a person quit smoking through many techniques. One is by suggesting that cigarette smoke will cause him to feel nauseous, meaning that every time somebody lights up a stick, the patient will start to feel dizzy and may even feel like throwing up.

Insomniacs, or people having trouble with sleeping, have been said to get their first night's sound sleep after being treated through hypnosis. Testimonials have also asserted that hypnotism has improved their capacity to learn, the sharpness of their memory, their performance in sports, or their intelligence.

Behaviour can also be modified with speech defects, physical limitations, and your personality experiencing dramatic changes. Your whole life can make a turnaround with the help of hypnosis. Sounds outstanding, but is hypnotism that effective?

Yes and No.

Yes, hypnotism has been used as part of the treatment and therapy of various physical and psychological conditions. Through its ability to tap into the subconscious and to intensify focus and concentration, hypnosis can help you be more in tune with your intellectual and emotional capacity, thus helping you modify your habits and behaviours, or wield more control over the way you think and analyze.

But no, it is not the cure-all for your problems. It is not proven to be effective every time and, in my experience, it has much more to do with the other things that a person is using to address whatever they are working on.

Tanya would be a perfect example of what this means. As you read through this chapter and the rest of the book, you will discover the power of the alchemy of mindset, body tools, and the conviction of the person who is asking for healing.

So Then Can You Hypnotize Me to Believe in It?

Webster's New International Dictionary defines hypnosis as "the induction of a state resembling sleep or somnambulism, which is called hypnosis or hypnotic sleep; also, loosely – the induced state of hypnosis."

There are degrees of hypnosis, which have been characterized as "lethargic, cataleptic, and somnambulistic hypnosis; and again, simply as light and heavy hypnotic sleep, with corresponding variations in suggestibility."

However, Encyclopedia Britannica further states, "there remains no generally acceptable explanation for hypnosis, though one prominent theory focuses on the possibility of discrete dissociative states affecting portions of consciousness."

The word hypnosis is derived from the Greek word *Hypnos*, meaning sleep. Hypnotism is often presumed to facilitate someone going under a state of reduced consciousness while remaining awake. The general behaviour of those under hypnosis is that they become extremely positive and open to suggestions through achieving a high level of relaxation.

Daydreaming is another activity likened to hypnotism, where, depending on how light the trance is, a person looks oblivious to his surroundings yet experiencing heightened imagination.

There are two ways by which hypnosis is performed: (1) hetero-hypnosis, where a hypnotist induces a state of being in trance and being open to suggestions; and (2) autohypnosis, where the state is self-induced.

The results are the same. A post-hypnotic suggestion is any suggestion that is carried out a period of time after hypnosis.

Believe it or not, we experience being hypnotized every day. Following the definition of hypnosis as being in a trance-like state, or intensely focusing on a particular activity/subject, we tune out almost everything else internally and otherwise.

Ever been so engrossed with a movie or a book that you did not immediately notice someone calling you? Reading, writing, and closely listening to a recording are examples of activities that can put us in a light trance and alter our attention so that we can become extremely attentive to these experiences and subsequently we unconsciously shut off outside subjects vying for our attention. Another example would be driving home and not remembering driving the car.

Furthermore, we sometimes become so affected by the imaginary world of a daydream or a chapter of a book that our emotions take over. We cry over an affecting song, feel fear as the villain gets near the hero's hiding place, or even scream over a particularly frightening scene.

This kind of phenomenon, referred to as self-hypnosis, is so common and so human of a trait that Milton Erickson, a hypnotism expert in the 20th century, concluded that people hypnotize themselves daily.

Note then that this kind of "everyday trance" is different from the trance brought about by deep hypnosis and is comparable to that relaxed mental state between wakefulness and sleep.

There is also a difference between autohypnosis, where the state of extreme suggestibility is self-induced, and hetero-hypnosis, where it is induced by a hypnotist or another person. In the end, both have value and, if you doubted your ability to be hypnotized, consider this is the proof you needed to become a believer. It happens frequently and naturally, but can also be created and induced.

Studies suggest that, on average, 25 out of 100 people can be hypnotized very easily. Almost all children belong to this group, as they are perceived to be highly susceptible to suggestions. This ratio varies according to the hypnotist's personality, technique, and experience. The success of the hypnotist also depends on the subject's personality, attention span, and current mental status. Interestingly, while it seems rational that people with high intellect cannot be easily hypnotized because of their capacity to process all information that gets into their brain, the opposite is true. It is believed that intelligent people are also the most creative, thus they can easily associate the hypnotist's wordplay with their own visual or sensory representations.

In Conclusion

At the end of the day, if you are considering using hypnosis as a tool for healing or change, the most important aspects will be that you believe in the capacity of hypnosis to help you heal, trust your therapist, "allow" them to induce and invite you into a trance, and commit to making the changes necessary and leveraging multiple tools that will get you where you want to go.

Philosopher Rene Descartes once said, "I think therefore I am." Following his discourse that anything is real once you set your mind to it then, indeed, hypnosis may be a logical step to achieving the best version of yourself.

The power of the mind and the subconscious is as boundless and generous as your dreams. Tapping that power through hypnosis is looking inside yourself and knowing your capabilities. It means understanding yourself, the people around you, and the world you live in. It is realizing that life and living are never constant. It is appreciating that we always aspire for change and that change happens from your willingness, your initiative, your hard work, and your perseverance.

Remember: Change is a verb. It fulfills its meaning once you act on it.

You may have realized by now that, ultimately, **IT ALL DEPENDS ON YOU.**

You have the power within you and no one can take it away from you. Self-hypnosis helps you unleash and harness that power and working with a therapist simply increases the odds of success.

Chemotherapy

"Successful people ask better questions, and as a result get better answers."

~ Tony Robbins

After surviving a month's worth of chemotherapy combined with radiation, it was time to move on to a heavier dosage of chemotherapy. Once a month, on average, I would get the well-organized blister package of capsules; however, after completing my first round of chemo, neither my white nor my red blood cell counts would go up high enough, no matter what I tried. Because of this, they reduced the dose of chemotherapy and I ended up getting a lesser dose for the remainder of the time. I struggled with this the first time through with Lymphoma, I simply couldn't get my counts to come back fast enough.

One thing that I liked this time around, was the fact that my chemotherapy could be taken before bed. That way, I would hopefully be asleep during any nausea that I may have felt. If there is something that you are not comfortable with, like one of the possible side effects from a medication, ask more questions and see if there's something else that can be done instead. For example, you don't have to live with bad constipation from an anti-nausea drug taken with chemotherapy. If there is an alternative option, ask and see. I was able to change to a higher level of anti-nausea drug and made it through with no constipation. I learned this lesson all too well earlier, I would get constipated for almost a week! No thank you! Not happening again!

I started listening to a new hypnosis from Rae-ann, owner of Integrity Seminars, who mentally supported me through this healing process. Tapping into the subconscious mind was doing wonders for me.

Action Step:

Ask. Ask. Ask lots of questions! What we don't know, we don't know. Sometimes all it takes to make your life a bit easier is you asking the right question.

Hair or No Hair? – That is the Question!

"Sometimes the biggest act of COURAGE is a small one."

~ Lauren Raffo

Two weeks into radiation, my hair had begun steadily falling out in large clumps daily. In the morning, I would brush my hair and the part that looked like a tangled mess was the part that would slide out right into the comb. Hair was everywhere and I constantly had to vacuum my couch and my sweaters. It was getting frustrating, so I decided I had to do something and, oh man, was I emotional about it!

I was agonizing over whether I should cut all my hair off or keep the bottom parts that were still hanging on so that, when I wore a hat, it looked like I still had my hair. That sounds crazy, I know.

It had been coming out for a couple of weeks and I thought it was rather funny that they told me that my hair would NOT fall out during radiation. Hmmm, very interesting. I laughed in my head about this because I thought that I could get away with not necessarily looking like someone who was going through cancer! Well, I guess I was wrong.

After many tears, I made the ultimate decision to let the hair go. There wasn't much left anyway. My sister-in-law trimmed it off for me and, I have to say, it was the right decision. Even though it was a very sensitive topic for me, having been there and done that already, I had felt good about this dramatic decision afterward. At least, with this solution, I wouldn't have to vacuum my clothes and the carpets every single day. When faced with this decision, let the hair go. You and your vacuum can thank me for that one later.

Five months after radiation, my hair did start to grow back and I also found all the missing hair in my vacuum! What a fun surprise that day was!

Action Step:

Be brave and let the hair go. Bald is beautiful and, let's face it, you are amazing any way you slice it! Be proud of yourself and who you are no matter what. Write down one nice compliment that you LOVE about yourself. It can be anything!

Trismus? Never Heard of it Until Today

"Gratitude unlocks the fullness of life. It turns what we have into enough."

~ Melody Beattle

Trismus? What is that? After talking with my personal trainer about some mouth mobility issues, I was having, she told me that I must have Trismus. This is when you can't open your mouth more than 35mm and was caused by my brain surgery.

I noticed this first when in the hospital. I couldn't open my mouth wide enough to eat large bites of food. I thought that it would simply go away. Today, I am very thankful for the mobility I still have.

When I went to see the physical therapist at the Cross Cancer Institute, she told me that I was lucky, and I still had 34% out of 45% of my mobility left in my jaw. Most people leave the hospital only at 11%, so I consider myself thankful in this respect. I do however wish someone at the hospital would have told me about this before I left. After all, I was only there for 17 days, I guess it just never came up.

Action Step:

For any medical procedure you may need to get done, write down a list of questions so you remember what you want to say. If you aren't happy with the answers, ask another doctor. Also, ask the right questions to the right person.

Vitamin C IV Therapy

"Trust your gut intuition."

~ Danielle Beaulieu

On the last day of 2020, I spent the morning going through Vitamin C IV therapy, which was something I had never tried before. Vitamin C IV therapy is when you are given a high dosage of Vitamin through an IV. It sometimes plays a role in cancer treatment. This is my personal experience with this procedure.

For the whole twenty minutes, the needle and my arm ended up hurting. I realized that this was a low dose Vitamin C IV therapy and, usually, I would be asked to do a higher dose.

This is not exactly an inexpensive treatment to have with it ranging from $180 to $300 a session in addition to paying for a naturopath. Lots of people have gone and continue to go this route; however, at this time, had I chose to continue forward with this treatment, my one good vein would've let me know it wasn't a good idea. I had to start learning to trust my thoughts and my feelings.

Health practitioners recommend doing this treatment three times a week, but not during chemotherapy. If you're not able to do it three times a week, it may not have the best success for you. Do your research and ask a doctor first to find out if it is good for the specific type of cancer that you have.

Some people say that it is good and others say that it might not be good for you, depending on your cancer. Ask lots of questions and then decide for yourself if this was a therapy that you wanted to try.

Having previously gone through Chemotherapy IV treatments during Lymphoma, this process ended up damaging the veins in my left arm. Luckily or unluckily, this happened during my last chemo session for that particular cancer. Your experience may be different from mine as with anything. Our bodies are not all the same and can react differently. Be sure to make the decision for yourself based on your body and on what you can afford to do financially.

Action Step:

Talk to people, investigate this therapy, and make your choice if this is something that you would like to invest in. Having only one good vein in my arm made my choice easier. It was time to trust myself.

Principle of Healing II

Increase Your Immune System and Strengthen Your Body

Our bodies want good products. This is how we LIVE to be our best or not so much. Keeping in mind, we also have a strong passion to be happy with LIVING our lives.

Food and Supplements

"Let food be thy medicine and medicine be thy food."

~Hippocrates

After being given the Stage 4 cancer label, I knew I wanted to change my diet.

I can say that my past food choices sometimes weren't the best. As an entrepreneur, my focus had shifted to the business and not always prepping my healthy meals. It's safe to say that I was never a great cook. I only learned about healthy eating after going thru cancer a few times. Maybe that stemmed from my mom's traditional English cooking, which never interested me, unless it was sauerkraut and sausage night. Then, I knew it was time to invite myself over to dinner or "coincidentally" arrive at my parent's door on that night. Yes, my timing was impeccable.

I'm not saying I was a terrible eater as I did eat well most of the time; however, consistency and some new diet changes would make it a little more challenging for me now. This new diet change is getting better on the daily.

I have never read so many labels in my life! Grocery store trips took on a whole new meaning, trying to read all the labels and avoid sugar as much as possible while keeping sodium on the low to no sodium side. Soon, my grocery shopping consisted of the same foods repeatedly. Trying to eat everything organic was just too expensive and I soon

77

realized that I had to cut some of my costs, hence the Dirty Dozen and the Clean Fifteen.

EWG'S DIRTY DOZEN FOR 2021

1. Strawberries
2. Spinach
3. Kale, collard, and mustard greens
4. Nectarines
5. Apples
6. Grapes
7. Cherries
8. Peaches
9. Pears
10. Bell and hot peppers
11. Celery
12. Tomatoes

EWG'S CLEAN FIFTEEN FOR 2021

1. Avocados
2. Sweet corn
3. Pineapple
4. Onions
5. Papaya
6. Frozen sweet peas (frozen)
7. Eggplant
8. Asparagus
9. Broccoli
10. Cabbage
11. Kiwi
12. Cauliflower
13. Mushrooms
14. Honeydew melon
15. Cantaloupes

When it came to taking supplements, anyone who knows me knows I will take them every day, religiously. When creating a new healthy habit, doing it now and then isn't going to cut it! Supplements or whole food products only work if you take them correctly and consistently! I can't stress this point enough. They won't work if you aren't taking them.

Here are some of the recommendations I followed:

- Vitamin B12 (since going vegetarian)
- Flax oil
- Iron supplement
- Greens
- Magnesium
- Vitamin D3

Recommendations from the Certified Holistic Cancer Practitioners Course:

Foods to avoid:

- Alcohol
- Sugar
- White flour
- Dairy
- Trans Fats
- Processed foods
- Reduce Meat intake
- Hydrogenated Oils

Foods to include:

- Greens, Veggies
- Fruits
- Water

- Healthy fats: avocado, nuts, coconut oil
- Organic: pesticide-free, antibiotic-free, non-GMO
- Natural sweeteners- raw honey, Stevia, coconut sugar, maple syrup, xylitol
- Gluten-free foods
- Mushrooms
- Green tea
- Legumes, nuts, and seeds
- Garlic
- Beets
- Bone Broth

Cancer-Fighting Herbs & Spices:

- Turmeric
- Astragalus
- Feverfew
- Goldenseal
- Echinacea
- Milk thistle
- Red clover
- Wheatgrass
- Pau d'arco
- Cat's claw
- Oregano
- Cayenne
- Ginger
- Cinnamon

Eat a high fibre diet:

- Avocados
- Berries
- Coconut
- Veggies

- Beans and Legumes
- Nuts/Seeds/Grains: Chia Seeds, Flax Seeds, Quinoa

Tip: Nuts and Seeds

If you have issues digesting nuts, try soaking them in water before you consume them. I was having issues with nuts and seeds, and this really made a difference for me. Nuts contain phytic acid and soaking them in water helps to break down this phytic acid– therefore helping your body digest them. Every nut and seed can be soaked for various times and possibly dehydrated. Cashews only need about two hours whereas almonds need about eight hours. Use clean filtered water to soak them in and rinse them thoroughly with clean filtered water after soaking. Do a search online and see what to do with your favourite nut or seed.

Extra Tips:

- Make sure you are getting enough protein, especially when giving up meat
- Try teas (green tea, peppermint, ginger, chamomile, black licorice) over coffee
- Drink lots of water! Lots!
- Get enough iron checks with your doctor, especially if you are not eating meat. You can try kidney beans, baked beans, Ezekiel bread, and spinach to help.
- Start your morning with a high fibre meal, sorry no donuts.
- Drink apple cider vinegar– 1-2 tablespoons in a glass of water; a little maple syrup can be added (*Note – Any other chapters that mention honey, you can switch this to organic

maple syrup, which contains enzymes and potassium that can give you a boost.)

- Probiotics (*Note – if you are currently having treatments your doctor may suggest NO probiotics. A safe alternative I used was coconut yogurt until I could go back on them again). Take your probiotics at dinner to be most effective.
- Lots of Antioxidants!

Keep in mind these are recommendations and what your body wants might be different. For me, I knew that every time I had anything with tomato in it would upset my stomach, so I stopped eating tomatoes and anything related to it, including ketchup. After that, I discovered that chia seeds also caused issues for me, so they went too.

A few people have suggested eating right for your blood type. Oddly enough a lot of the things on this list did apply to me and some didn't, so make your own choices and LISTEN to your body. Keeping a food journal will help you understand and be mindful of what your body needs to be energized. This is a learning process.

Tip: Purchase organic frozen berries and put some in a glass dish overnight so you can use them the next day. I'm currently loving blackberries because they are so juicy! You can add the leftover juice to your water for extra flavour too. So good!

Juice Plus+ Whole Food Products

I wanted to be able to offer others a safe nutrition product that they could take during chemotherapy. I never thought that the person taking them would end up being me! These products are filled with fruits and vegetables and are a great way to fill the gap between what you are eating and what you should be eating. For a picky veggie eater, who will remain nameless, it is a great option to have. I always say it's like juicing, minus the sugar and the messy cleanup, which was perfect and easy for me.

I took the Juice Plus+ products throughout all my treatments. My sister-in-law brought them to me after my Craniotomy in the hospital. I was approved to take the shakes and the capsules throughout my radiation and chemotherapy while continuing to have a shake almost every day. I loaded it up with lots of superfood goodness.

I will admit that I became a bit analytical over this product because I was frustrated. I wasn't getting the lab results that I had hoped. When I ran out, it would be a few weeks before my next order arrived. After being off it for a few weeks, I noticed the difference in my body. To my happiness, I realized it was keeping my body healthier on the inside. You don't know what you got until it's gone!

When I was back on it again, my head felt less heavy, I felt more energy and overall wellness. I have heard a lot of people say that they aren't sure what it is doing until they go on it again after being off of it... Nothing is better than whole food, aka real food, nutrition.

For more information and to find out how to get free meal plans monthly, see the resources section.

Water

Water contains every colour of the rainbow and is super good for your body, especially when dealing with dis-ease. We want to keep those toxins moving OUT of our bodies. Stay well hydrated!

Cancer loves a dry environment, so drink water regularly. Be cautious of some of the juices that are out there, which are loaded with sugar. Review the label before you purchase. Again, I've never read so many labels in my life!

If you are on chemotherapy, you will need to increase your water intake even more as it will dry out your skin. Find a nice natural moisturizer such as Tamanu oil- approximately $15 at your health store- and apply regularly. Here are a few of water's amazing benefits:

- Cushions your joints
- Provides extra moisture for your blood and brain
- Assists with digestion
- Prevents dehydration- if you feel thirsty, you are already dehydrated.
- Boosts skin health
- Maintains blood pressure
- Airways need it, great for allergies
- Helps your body use minerals and nutrients more effectively
- Better exercise performance
- Great for the kidneys

Lemon Water

This Vitamin C-packed fruit is great in warm water first thing in the morning. This gets the digestive system moving, reduces possible bloating, cleans out any toxins that may be stuck there, and is great for the skin. It also energizes our bodies! More benefits are that it is antibacterial, antiviral, boosts the immune system, and helps cleanse your liver.

I've heard stories of some people who've had liver cancer that may have improved after having a daily routine of warm lemon water for over three months. I found the trick to getting warm water and having leftover water for a tea. Boil the water, pour some in a mug for your tea along with an inch of boiled water already squeezed with lemon in your glass for your lemon water. Drink through a reusable straw to save your teeth from the acid from the lemon. Sip up!

Tip: You can also use lemon essential oil instead. See Essential Oils Section.

For the Love of Tea

I've never really been a tea drinker before in my life. My mom, on the other hand, really loved enjoying a good cup of tea. She even collected those beautiful teacups! I kept those Red Rose ceramic tea figurines from ages ago.

Now, I have started to enjoy tea because a lot of them are anti-inflammatory, which is a bonus. Some of these teas are:

Green Tea - Loaded with antioxidants. This tea is known as being one of the healthiest teas available. Not only is it good for your brain, but the L-theanine in it also crosses the blood-brain barrier. This amino acid is also in some of the supplements I used to help me sleep at night. There are so many health benefits to this powerhouse tea. It may also reduce your risk of getting cancer.

Ginger Tea - Great for digestive issues, headaches and nausea. This tea is loaded with antioxidants and is anti-inflammatory- two great things that we need in our diets.

Peppermint Tea - Another tea known for its digestive and headache-solving benefits with the bonus of having fresh breath. Think about how, when you brush your teeth with a minty flavoured toothpaste, it kind of gives you a little bit of a Zing. This tea may also give you a boost of energy. Anti-inflammatory, antiviral, and loaded with antioxidants- again! This tea is another powerhouse to have in your cupboard.

Black Licorice Tea – I don't know about you, but I love the taste of black licorice and have since I was a kid. This tea tastes just like it and is a nice treat. Among its health benefits, it's antibacterial and antiviral. It may soothe your sore throat and is known to help an upset stomach or to aid during acid reflux. The bonus of this tea is that it might help prevent you from getting any cavities. The tea that is, not the candy! Give it a try and see for yourself.

Inflammatory Foods

Inflammatory foods are those that we don't want to be eating while dealing with dis-ease. Here is a list of foods to reduce or eliminate in your diet:

- White bread and flours- use almond flour
- Red meats, hot dogs, sausages
- Sugar and Sodas
- Margarine
- Fried Foods

Eat More Anti-Inflammatory Foods:

- Fruits
- Tomatoes
- Green Vegetables
- Nuts
- Olive Oil
- Avocado- a healthy fat
- Mushrooms
- Peppers
- Fatty fish
- Dark chocolate

Action Step:

Meal prepping is a great way to plan out your week of meals because you'll know you're getting the nutrients that your body is craving. Using this list, make your own food list and see what you can fit into your daily routine. When you have a list before going to the grocery store, it will be much easier and will prevent you from making unhealthy choices. Keep in mind, everything in moderation, though. Sometimes I would treat myself to a Swiss Chalet dinner because it would always put a smile on my face. We still need happiness in our lives too! We don't always need to be someone dealing with a dis-ease. Give yourself a break!

Microgreens & Medicine Valley Farms
Jesse Wood-Schatz

"Always do your best. What you plant now you will harvest later."

~ Og Mandino

Medicine Valley Farms is a family farm located in Lacombe County, Alberta. We focus on growing microgreens as a healthy and affordable food option for those located in central Alberta. We offer microgreens year-round to residents, restaurants, and grocery stores in Edmonton, Red Deer, Sylvan Lake, and surrounding areas. Our mission is to support local food security, environmentally sustainable practices, and the wellness of our communities.

Microgreens are regular vegetable seeds that are grown to the first set of leaves and then harvested around the seven to fourteen-day mark. Rather than picking the fruit or vegetable from a mature plant, harvesting at an early stage results in tender seedlings that contain all the genetic information of their fully-grown counterparts. Microgreens allow us to consume all elements of the plant minus its roots. As a result, we can consume a high concentration of nutrients with only a small number of greens.

Researchers with the University of Maryland College of Agriculture and Natural Resources (AGNR) and the United States Department of Agriculture (USDA) suggest that microgreens can be four to forty times more nutrient-dense than their fully grown vegetable counterparts (Binder). Packed with vitamins, minerals, and other phytonutrients, microgreens are highly concentrated superfoods that contain beneficial properties linked to the reduction of the risk and progression of chronic illness, such as cardiovascular disease and cancer (Xiao and Zhenlei).

Beyond the convenient ability to increase the nutritional value of almost any meal, microgreens are equally powerful in flavour and appearance. Offering a wide range of flavour profiles, colours, and textures, microgreens elevate the taste and presentation of a plate. For example, sunflower shoots have large, crunchy green leaves with a nutty and slightly sweet taste. Broccoli microgreens are soft, smaller, and have a mild, peppery, flavour. A red radish's dark purple and green leaves are eye-catching and pack a pungent, spicy kick.flavour

Short, indoor growing cycles allow us to consistently deliver fresh greens year-round. Short transportation distances mean that we never have to use preservatives and fossil fuel emissions are reduced. Growing microgreens does not require the use of large machines nor preserving chemicals. The process requires humans, lights, soil, and water. Our operations allow us to deliver superior freshness without compromise and we harvest and deliver within twenty-four hours, so the microgreens stay good for up to two weeks!

Before her diagnosis, Tanya was working with us on developing our farm's website. In the final stages of finishing the website, we received the news of Tanya's diagnosis. After helping us tremendously with our business, we felt compelled to offer our microgreens as a way of supporting Tanya on her journey. We started delivering weekly packages. Tanya enjoyed them and implemented them into her regular diet.

Scientific research supports the claim that microgreens possess anticancer properties. Sulforaphane is a Sulphur-rich compound found highly concentrated in cruciferous vegetables such as kale, broccoli, cabbage, cress, and Bok choy (Coyle). Sulforaphane is a potent antioxidant and cellular detoxifier that protects the body against carcinogens, and it is associated with supporting cognitive, heart, and digestive health (Coyle).

Broccoli and broccoli brassica blend are what we frequently deliver to Tanya. Broccoli and its link to cancer prevention is relatively well-researched. Studies have shown broccoli microgreens can contain up to ten times more sulforaphane than mature broccoli (Neves).

Daikon radish is another variety of microgreens with exceptional nutritional properties. One hundred grams of daikon radish microgreens contain approximately 6.1 mg of provitamin A (β-carotene), and 87.4mg of vitamin E (α-tocopherol) (Xiao, Zhenlei). According to the Dietary Reference Intakes on the Government of Canada website, this equates to approximately 678% of an adult's recommended daily allowance (RDA) for provitamin A, and 588% of the RDA for vitamin E (Xiao, Zhenlei).

Provitamin A carotenoids have been known to have beneficial properties relating to immune, endocrine, and metabolic activities (Koon). Vitamin E is believed to be important in protecting cells from oxidative stress, regulating immune function, and maintaining cell integrity (National Center for Biotechnology Information).

Microgreens are a nutritional powerhouse, and the full range of their benefits is continuing to be researched. We are excited to introduce microgreens to those who are newly discovering their intense flavour and potency, and we are equally excited to supply the highest quality greens to those who are long-time micro lovers.

My ultimate goals in life are to live every day with purpose and to build strong relationships and community. I have always wanted to work for myself, but I needed to find something that fit in my heart and served my community. Microgreens have checked all the boxes: locally, sustainably grown food that supports the health and wellness of others.

For me, being an entrepreneur is about being able to give back. At the core of everything I am doing as a business owner, is a desire to create opportunities for my family and community. To me, that means following practices that are centred around landscape and wildlife conservation, funding community/grassroots projects, and donating to Land Back initiatives. It also involves helping community members directly, which is why seeing the incredibly positive effects that our microgreens are having in Tanya's life fills me with joy and gratitude. In the future, it is my goal to create opportunities that I have been fortunate to have myself for others, including offering scholarships and opportunities for underprivileged youth.

Action Step:

If you're like me and have always been a picky eater, especially when it comes to vegetables, this is a great way to get vegetables into your body at a higher concentration without having to go through any kind of yuck factor I can still hear my mom's voice now, "Tanya! Eat your vegetables!" while my friends laugh out loud at this comment.

Vitamin D3

"Every sunrise brings HOPE."

~ Unknown
~ Sarah's favorite quote

Vitamin D does a body good! There may be some evidence that Vitamin D is a preventative for cancer. It is also important for maintaining healthy bones, keeping us happier. Depending on what's going on in your life, your Vitamin D intake will vary. In my case, I was getting tested regularly to see if my Vitamin D intake was low and it was. I was deficient and needed to take a higher dose for some time. This test can be done by anyone at your blood lab, and it costs under $100. Then you will know exactly what your body needs.

Some known deficiency issues are:

- Cancer
- Cognitive function in older adults
- Weakened bone strength
- Muscle weakness
- Cardiovascular disease
- Skin issues such as psoriasis, dermatitis, vitiligo

You can increase your Vitamin D intake by taking drops or capsules in a dosage that was recommended by your doctor or health practitioner. It has been shown to also be more effective when taken with a higher fat meal. See the list below for more ways you can get Vitamin D into your diet. If you are going vegan or vegetarian, you can omit some of the meat suggestions from your diet. I omitted most of these because it was what MY body wanted.

- Salmon
- Beef
- Tuna
- Eggs
- Mushrooms
- Tofu
- Some fortified cereals
- Fortified almond or rice milks

Another way to feel this Vitamin Boost is by using a light therapy device. I purchased one off Amazon and used it during breakfast on those indoor darker days. I would sit down, enjoy my coconut yogurt with berries and hemp hearts, and soak up the energy!

Skin Cancer

A great way to get Vitamin D naturally is to go for a walk and soak up the beautiful sunshine – with limited exposure, though. I can still picture my mom marching down to the beach to remind my friend Sarah and me to use sunscreen. I don't think I listened very well. Sunburn city! Ouch! That was painful.

Let's talk about skin cancer for a minute. Two of my four cancers were skin cancer. Vitamin D from the sunshine can be good, but damaging for our skin as well. I remember getting sunburned a few times in my younger years when we thought it was cool to soak in the sun. My pale white skin disagreed with this fact. In my twenties, I had a multi-coloured mole on my left ankle that turned out to be Melanoma, which I had surgery to remove. Over the years, Basal Cell cancer happened in my life twice, which happened to be a mark that did not seem to heal. If you are unsure about a spot that you have, get it checked out by a doctor to be safe. I tell you, I'm a super sleuth now to skin cancer. I feel like I could spot it a mile away!

When you know you have to be out in the sun for a longer period, consider getting some UV-protected clothing. They have shirts for adults to wear and UV protection shirts and bottoms for kids. Protect your beautiful skin.

There are a few foods that can also help protect your skin too, such as blueberries, watermelon, and green leafy vegetables. They would need to be consumed regularly to have some sun-protective effects. Antioxidant power! Please note this does not equal applying natural sunscreen to the body.

Action Step:

The sun is such a healer for our bodies, and it makes us feel so much better. Allow the sunshine to come in through your eyes for at least 10 to 15 minutes each day. So, are you going for a walk? Throw some earbuds in and listen to music that makes you feel good. Good music = good mood.

Natural Products

"When consumed for its antioxidant properties, dark chocolate has less fat than broccoli."

~ Unknown

I have used natural products for many years now. Interestingly, many of the big-name brands are now producing paraben-free or SLS free products. So, it makes you wonder- there must be something to this!

The key point here is to think about all the products you are putting on your skin and spraying in your environment. Ask yourself, "Are these healthy for my body?" Then when you go to the grocery store or the health store, make a different choice. You can choose a different product- it's totally up to you.

Think about what you do after you have a shower. You put on a whole bunch of lotions or creams. Are they clean? Now you've just created a toxic environment in your body, which is not what we want. We want to reduce the number of toxins that are going into our body through our skin and into our bloodstream.

When your immune system is already low, you can be susceptible to anything from any of the products and we want your immune system to be strong. We don't want your body to be susceptible to bacterial, fungal infections, viruses, and especially not cancer.

The chemicals from these products get into our blood from smelling, touching, or tasting something that contains them. Our body has to find a way to secrete these toxins. If they're not able to do this in a fast enough time, then disease can happen.

Things that can happen when we have a weakened immune system are headaches, muscle weakness, vision problems, sleeping problems, organ damage, mental problems, heart disease, immune system breakdown, hair loss, allergic reactions, memory loss, premature aging, joint pain, and cancer.

Here's a list of products that you might want to swap out for natural ones:

- Shampoo, conditioner, hair spray, dry shampoo
- Moisturizer
- Face and body creams
- Makeup
- Deodorant
- Soaps
- Body Wash
- Sunscreen

Here's a list of products you might not even think about replacing initially:

- Detergent
- Dishwasher products
- Toothpaste
- Mouthwash
- Sanitary Napkins
- Perfume
- Nail Polish
- Air freshener sprays
- Fabric softener

This is an easy way to reduce the toxins seeping into your body through your skin. Another way is to add more antioxidants into your diet daily to assist your body in detoxification. Some of these are apples, blueberries, berries, green tea, green veggies, and nuts.

Antioxidants can strengthen your immune system by fighting off free radicals– these are the bad guys that can create disease within the body when they get out of control. Helping with detoxification, improve vitamin D absorption, protect skin integrity, and are also anti-inflammatories, which is a great thing when dealing with a dis-ease. We don't want inflammation in our bodies. That isn't a good thing!

Action Step:

Make a list of what antioxidants you are taking daily. Do you need to add more? Also, make a list of household or personal products that you can slowly start to swap out. The key is that you don't have to do everything all at once. Check things off your list as you go. Your body will thank you!

Essential Oils
Karen Quinlan

"What you put out into the Universe you get in return, so make sure it's fabulous!"

~ Karen Quinlan

Hello, my friends! I hope you don't mind that I call you that, friends just make the world a brighter and happier place, don't they?

Thank you for picking up this book, maybe skimming over the back cover, flipping through some pages, and ultimately deciding it's for you or for someone you love.

I would also like to thank my dear friend, Tanya, for considering me worthy of sharing my insight, education, and passion for essential oils.

Tanya and I met because a mutual friend of ours thought we shared a lot in common and, as it turns out, we do! Not only do we both believe in the power of food as medicine, positive thought, welcoming good energies into our lives, and releasing the old, but we also believe in a balance between modern medicine and holistic alternatives. We are both passionate about sharing as much of our education and experiences with others as possible. Hoping to light a little fire of burning desire for you to become your best, healthiest, and most authentic selves. I couldn't be prouder of this inspirational woman for getting this information out there and into your hands. Mwah Tanya, love you my friend!

My journey into holistic alternatives began in 2006 when my son, who was four and a half years old at the time, had a toxic allergic reaction to mold. His immune system shut down, he could barely move off the couch, and he became allergic to what felt like everything– dairy, wheat, corn, soy, eggs, yeast, sugar, trees outside, snow, mold and mold… ugh. It was an overwhelming and exhausting time. No mother wants to watch this happen to their child. Our new normal became reading labels, buying very basic foods, and ALWAYS, ALWAYS bringing his own food with him everywhere he went– school lunches, friend's birthday parties, sporting events, and even the mall food court! I plopped myself in front of the internet and researched doctors, diets, and treatment plans.

I am beyond grateful to my friends who made suggestions and pointed me in the direction of holistic healing. Or should I say "Whole-istic" healing? Because healing the "whole" body is where the magic happens.

It was through using various tools like Biofeedback, Live Blood Analysis, Emotional Freedom Technique (EFT), Chiropractors, Acupuncture, Osteopathy, Homeopathy, and Naturopathy, and his conviction to getting better, that my son was able to regain his health by the time he was six.

It's now thirteen years later and he's had several issues return here and there. Along with his sisters and then myself with Hashimoto's and Adrenal Fatigue. As I look back on the years of lemons we were given, I like to focus on the big jug of lemonade right in front of us today. Each of those lemons provided a new tool, insight, perspective, and healing modality, setting us up with a great foundation moving forward. As my kids become young adults, preparing to leave my cozy little nest soon (sad, crying emoji face), I am happy they have a choice of solid fundamentals that they can take with them!

One of these super amazing tools for sweetening that big jug of lemonade is Essential Oils.

My first experience with essential oils was at my daughter's volleyball game. If you have ever watched a lot of volleyball, you know your neck can crank from left to right and there are a ton of whistles blowing. I mean A. LOT. OF. WHISTLES! My neck and shoulders knotted right up, and I had a doozie of a headache. You know the feeling! Thankfully, another mom whipped out a sample of soothing essential oil rub in a little blue square packet. My awesome hubby rubbed it into my shoulders, and it was **CRAZY AMAZING** how fast I felt relief with such a small amount. I immediately needed to know more about these oils. I started attending a lot of classes in the area to learn about essential oils and came out being educated about the TOXINS in our everyday lives too.

Did you know that the average North American woman uses approximately 20 toxic products before she even leaves the house in the morning? Each of those products can contain more than a dozen chemicals in each bottle. Take a second to check the labels on your products one day- facial cleansers, toners, serums, brighteners and tighteners, moisturizers, shampoo and conditioners, body soaps, hair smoothers, foams, gels and sprays, makeup, perfumes, and lip gloss. This is even before leaving your bathroom! Continue to your kitchen and think about cleaning supplies, then on to your laundry room with detergents, etc.

Today, the average person is in contact with roughly 550 synthetic chemicals in twenty-four hours, versus 134 synthetic chemicals five years ago. In 2018, there were 80,000 registered chemicals in the USA, and only 200 were fully tested for safety. Say WHAT?

Most people don't understand the consequences of these synthetic chemicals to our bodies and our minds. Many toxins are "Endocrine Disruptors", chemicals "act" like the natural estrogen we have in our bodies but start messing around with our hormones. Some are even called "Obesogens", fat-loving chemicals that store themselves in our fat cells. They can be responsible for unexplained weight gain, fatigue, moodiness, hot flashes, and poor memory. I don't know about you, but I have experienced each of these symptoms in extreme doses over the last few years.

So, what are you looking to avoid on your labels? Parabens, Phthalates, Fragrances, and BPAs are a great start.

Parabens are commonly used as preservatives to prevent the growth of harmful bacteria and mold in cosmetic and body care products like shampoos, face cleansers, body washes, lotions, and foundations. They absorb easily through the skin and mimic estrogen, interfering with hormone function for both women and men. Thankfully, many items are now coming out Paraben-Free.

Phthalates, one of the most widely used chemicals, are found in hundreds of products like shower curtains, kid's toys, dish soaps, laundry detergents, scented candles, and many of our personal care products. Phthalates are found in our much-loved fragrances and perfumes because they help the scent linger longer. The one word "Fragrance" can contain up to 4000 chemicals! Hard to believe but it's true. Since fragrances are protected as proprietary blends, these chemicals don't have to be named on the label. Instead, you will see "Fragrance", "Perfume", "Parfum", "Aroma", "Flavour", "Unscented". Think about where we continuously apply fragrances– on our neck and throat area. We're breathing them in and absorbing them through our skin and right into our thyroid and bloodstream heading to our brains. Thyroid Dysfunction is prevalent these days as well as Alzheimer's and Dementia. We have control over the products we choose to use and it's not too late to start removing phthalates from our homes.

BPA's, The plastic in a soft water bottle contains phthalates, but BPAs are found in plastics like your hard water bottles, food wrap, and food storage containers. These are linked to everything from breast and other cancers to reproductive problems and obesity, early puberty, and heart disease. Please don't allow plastic wrap to touch your food! The BPA's leach in and then you consume the food, making way for them to wreak havoc inside your body. Think about replacing your plastic water bottles and food storage containers with glass or stainless-steel containers.

I became hooked on replacing as many chemical products as possible with Mother Nature and gifts of the earth like essential oils. I started by

- Tossing out those nasty scented candles and swapping them with diffusers.
- Trashing my old cleaning supplies and replacing them with essential oils and vinegar or distilled water.
- Throwing that toxic box of dryer sheets straight into the garbage and using wool dryer balls with essential oils instead.
- Replacing the whole family's toxic body and hair care products with non-toxic solutions – they weren't happy with me about that one!

Oops. Sorry, not sorry!

I not only became passionate about non-toxic solutions, but obsessed you might say. I couldn't get enough education and enrolled at the Institute of Integrative Nutrition to become a Health Coach. Along with completing an Essential Oil Certification course and Environmental Toxins course which ran at the same time. It felt amazing to start ditching the toxins and incorporating essential oils into my home. I am here today to help educate and provide you with some non-toxic alternatives to your daily life.

I am going to use the rest of the chapter as an Introduction to Essential Oils Class. We'll begin with the fundamentals and move into the nitty-gritty and fun stuff. You can use essential oils to support your overall health and wellness too!

What are Essential Oils?

Let's keep this as simple as possible. Essential oils are the essence of a plant. The concentrated chemical compounds are hidden in a plant's roots, seeds, flowers, and bark. They give the plant its unique scent while protecting it from its environment and helping with pollination and other functions. If the oils do this for the plant, think of how they can also do this for us. Various parts of the plant are either steam-distilled or cold-pressed and are eventually delivered in the beautiful little bottles you see in stores and online today. These oils truly are gifts from the earth, providing us with valuable therapeutic remedies without addictive qualities.

Not all essential oils are created equal and I know the whole business can be a little overwhelming when you are trying to choose a brand. Every store seems to carry a different one. One easy thing to remember is that you probably won't find "quality" in the cheapest brands.

Grades of Essential Oils:

Food Grade

The food and flavour industry is the number one industry for essential oil consumption. For example, think about the peppermint flavoured chocolates you enjoy at Christmas.

This peppermint flavouring can contain a variety of additives or solvents to achieve a standard scent, smell, or taste so every bite is the same. The difference is if it's a natural flavouring that is essential oil based or an artificial flavouring that is chemical based. A chemical based flavouring is synthetic, but still based on the chemical structures of essential oils. (1) 98% of the essential oils produced today are either food grade used in food flavourings or perfume grade used in perfumes and cosmetics.

Therapeutic Grade

These oils refer to the purity and ability to achieve the desired result or health benefit one is looking for. They are grown indigenously in their native growing region, like lavender grown in Bulgaria and France, harvested at their peak performance, and distilled or cold-pressed with proper care taken with both temperature and time.

Does purity matter?

Pure, unadulterated essential oils are safer and more effective. Other oils can be contaminated and loaded with synthetic fillers which do more harm than good. Something to keep in mind while browsing is that low-quality essential oils also have warnings not to ingest them. Well, if you can't ingest a lemon oil that is supposed to be made from a lemon, it must have chemical or filler in it. Is it ok then to smell that oil and have those chemical compounds enter your nasal cavity and go up to your brain? It's important to think twice about the purity of the oil you are using.

Some companies may charge more for their oils than others. It costs more to have essential oils third-party tested to guarantee transparency, absence of toxins, contaminants, microorganisms, and other chemical residues in the final product for every single batch. I am more inclined to choose an essential oil brand with these checkmarks versus some much less expensive store-bought brand. The choice however is ultimately yours to make.

Consider this: It requires about 242,000 rose petals to distill approximately 5 ml of *Certified Pure Therapeutic Grade* Rose essential oil. Crazy, right? I can't even imagine how many roses that is. Incredible! It also takes a pound of peppermint leaves and flowering tops to create a 15 ml bottle of *Certified Pure Therapeutic Grade* Peppermint essential oil. That's a lot of plant matter and plants do matter.

Therapeutic grade essential oils are extremely potent, fifty to seventy-five times more powerful than herbs! "Less is More" is a good adage to remember when using essential oils. For example, one drop of *Certified Pure Tested Grade* peppermint essential oil in a cup of warm water is equivalent to roughly 28 cups of peppermint tea. A little does go a long way, so you'll want to remember that. It's not necessary to use more than a drop or two at a time. I know it can be tempting to shake that little bottle like salt on a juicy cob of corn at your family BBQ, but that's a huge waste of product and money. That's what also makes these oils affordable. A 15 ml bottle holds 250 drops of the essential oil. If you are using only a drop or 2 at a time, it can last a long time, and at pennies a drop.

How Can We Use Essential Oils?

There are three ways to use essential oils- aromatically, topically, and internally. Each person reacts to essential oils differently, and different methods of using them work better for some than for others. Different oils work better for some than others. It may take some trial and error to see what oils and oil combinations work best for you and your family, but this can be part of the fun. Make the most of it, enjoy your oils, and feel confident discussing your potential practices with your healthcare provider.

Aromatically means breathing in the oils. You can either use a diffuser to disperse the oil droplets into the air or place a drop or 2 in the palm of your hands, rub them together and take a few long inhales.

Imagine peeling an orange, the sweet zest sprays and sprinkles orange droplets on your fingers. Your mouth starts to water as you smell the sweetness, and you are ready for the burst of flavour on your taste buds. When you inhale these droplets, they go right into your olfactory system, which involves your amygdala and limbic system. This is where your primal brain is along with your mood, memory, and emotions that affect your brain. That is why memory and smells are tied together. Once in your bloodstream, the droplets also end up traveling up and down your spine and central nervous system, impacting your whole body.

Citrus Oils like Wild Orange are uplifting because they not only calm you down, but also cheer you up! To me, citrus oils are my sunshine oils. When I breathe them in, I feel wrapped up in a nice warm hug that just makes me feel good!

Topically means applying them directly to your skin for localized benefits from symptoms like warts, acne, inflammation, sore muscles and joints, burns, bites, belly aches and headaches, fevers, etc.

Some oils may be applied "neat", which means directly from the bottle to your skin. On the other hand, "diluting" essential oils with something like fractionated coconut oil, almond oil, olive oil, or other carrier oils helps "carry" the essential oil through the skin and to the source and is highly recommended instead of neat.

It takes approximately twenty seconds for a *Certified Pure Tested Grade* oil to be absorbed through your skin, two minutes for it to get into your bloodstream, and twenty minutes (more or less) for you to start noticing the effects. It's a little slower of a process when you dilute, but the carrier oil helps carry the essential oil deeper into your body.

If you ever need some digestive support from a hangover, eating too much Christmas dinner, cramps that come with your period, or nausea, applying diluted essential oils like peppermint or ginger directly to your stomach is a complete game changer! Applying essential oils to the areas in which you are experiencing pain and discomfort, as well as to the acupressure points on the bottoms of your feet, can provide a ton of relief. Take sinus headaches for example. We all know how annoying and painful these can be. Applying oils like peppermint and eucalyptus to the little pads under your toes can help support opening your sinuses up.

*It is never recommended to use oils, neat or diluted, directly in your eyes, ears, or nose. Also, certain oils are **"photosensitive"** and can react with your skin negatively under the sun. Citrus oils will do this, so it is recommended not to use these oils on your exposed skin and be under the sun within 12 hours- **Bergamot, Blood Orange, Lemon, Lime, Mandarin, Sweet Orange, Orange Leaf, Satsuma, Tangelo, Tangerine, Yuzu. (2)**

Ingestion means consuming essential oils by adding them to something you eat, drink, or take in a veggie capsule. When you ingest them, you get a complete systemic effect throughout your body. It does mean they need to go through your digestive tract and then outwards into your body. This process may take a little longer than applying them directly to your skin or area of concern if you are looking for more immediate relief.

Ingesting certain *Certified Pure Tested Grade* Essential oils can be done safely. If you eat fresh herbs, you're consuming micro doses of essential oils. Zesting a lemon or lime peel is the same as ingesting the essential oil. It's important to know which oils are safe to consume and that oils and water don't mix. If you were to add a drop of essential oil to a cup of water, you will notice the oil floating on the surface. I like to add a drop of ginger and lemon to a tad bit of honey first, then stir into boiling water for a great digestive supporting tea after dinner. The honey helps to blend the oils in and liquid stevia works nicely too.

Once inhaled, applied topically, or ingested, the ability of essential oils to penetrate a cell's membrane is amazing! Unlike bacteria, which float around outside your cells and in your bloodstream, a virus makes a home within your cells. Antibiotics can eliminate bacterial infections but can't penetrate through a cell's oily membrane to get at a pesky virus. Hence why you usually are told to rest and drink your mama's good old chicken noodle soup. Resting and drinking bone broth is a wise idea to battle a virus. Part of the therapeutic value of essential oils however, comes from their ability to absorb through the oily cell's membrane and attack the virus directly.

An essential oil alone can work wonders, but most times the outcome can be even better when paired up with other oils. It's synergy. The whole can be greater than the sum of its parts. Blending oils can be the icing on the cake, a grand-slam home run, or a triple threat.

Incorporating Essential Oils in Your Daily Life

Woohoo! Now, this is the fun part. Instead of reaching for over-the-counter store-bought medicine, cleaning supplies, or beauty and body care products, consider using essential oils. They provide natural relief, a clean home, and a healthier body, skin, and hair without overloading your system with synthetic substances.

Let's consider **Ten Top Alternatives** you can add to your home for healthier living. To make sure these oils don't sit unopened or unused in a closet somewhere, I encourage you to keep them out on your countertops, in your bathrooms, on your nightstand, at the office, in your gym bag and develop a daily ritual with them.

The star * beside an essential oil is a reminder that this oil is considered photosensitive and should not be applied to the skin before going out into the sun. Also, keep in mind, if I mention taking any of these oils internally, I am talking about *Certified Pure Tested Grade* essential oils that contain zero fillers.

Clary Sage- for the Ladies:

- Apply directly to your abdomen before those period cramps take your breath away. It cools inflammation and its antispasmodic properties help soothe muscle cramps. This oil is an absolute game changer during that sometimes painful time of the month.
- Apply this hormone balancing rollerball to your ovaries when you wake up, and before you go to bed, to support Hot Flashes, PMS, and other hormonal related symptoms. Use 10 drops of Clary Sage, 8 drops of Lavender, 8 drops of Geranium, 4 drops of Bergamot, and 4 drops of Ylang Ylang with fractionated coconut oil and then dispense in a 10ml rollerball.
- Cool your hot flashes with a couple of drops of Clary Sage and Ylang Ylang added to a tablespoon of castor oil. Add this to a piece of organic cotton and

apply it over your ovaries daily (search homemade Castor Oil Pack).

- Combine Clary Sage with Jojoba Oil with your skin care products to cool inflammation and also as a natural rash remedy.
- Diffuse next to your bed or rub a drop or two onto your neck and soles of your feet to calm, relax and prepare your body and mind for a restful nights' sleep. Add Vetiver, Lavender, Marjoram for an extra peaceful sleep.
- Increase blood circulation and lower blood pressure by relaxing the brain and arteries and rubbing the diluted oil onto your limbs and chest.

Eucalyptus:

- Add a couple of drops of Peppermint and Eucalyptus to a sponge while in the shower to open your airways and relieve congestion and sinus pressure. Mix equal parts with a carrier oil and apply to the chest for a homemade vapour rub. Diffuse Peppermint and Eucalyptus next to your bed to help you breathe better while you sleep. Eucalyptus is a super awesome oil for opening the airways and relieving congestion.
- Massage around your ear to help alleviate pain from an earache, Melaleuca (Tea Tree) helps as well.
- Diffuse during the day when you need help with feeling awake, energized, and focused, or add a couple drops to your temples or back of your neck.
- Diffuse while cleaning your home to help purify the air.
- Apply a couple of drops with a carrier oil to relieve the pain and itching of shingles.

- Treat wounds, burns, cuts, insect stings, sores, and scrapes by applying to the affected area twice daily. The antimicrobial and antiseptic properties help support healing.
- Add 15 drops of Lemon, 15 drops of Eucalyptus, ¼ cup white vinegar and 1 ¾ cup distilled water to a 16 oz dark glass spray bottle to use as an all-purpose cleaner.
- Combine a few drops of Lavender, Melaleuca (Tea Tree), and Eucalyptus to ¼ cup Epsom salt. Run warm bath water and empty the Epsom Salt mixture under the running water, then soak in the tub for 20 minutes. Not only is this relaxing, but the oils also get to work supporting your immune system. It's a Win-Win!
- Diffuse a couple of drops of Lemon, Eucalyptus, and Clove to help eliminate germs. Try this in a bathroom that is shared amongst multiple people.

Frankincense ~ The KING OF OILS ~ Your Go-To Oil:

- Add a drop of Frankincense to your non-toxic beauty care products to promote youthful, healthy skin, reducing imperfections. Any time any skin issue arises on my body, I apply Frankincense neat directly to the problem area a few times a day. Think of using it for stretch marks, scars, sunspots, and wrinkles.
- Diffuse Frankincense next to your bed to calm, relax and prepare your body and mind for a restful night's sleep, and/or rub onto the bottoms of your feet or back of neck and spine area. Add Vetiver, Lavender, Marjoram for an extra peaceful sleep.
- Rub a couple of drops onto the bottoms of your feet or pulse points to calm anxious feelings and ground you in the present moment.

- Add a drop of Lavender, Peppermint, and Frankincense to Aloe Vera Gel and rub gently over sunburnt skin.
- Massage into sore joints and muscles to improve circulation and fight inflammation.
- Diffuse Frankincense to help focus or unwind. It's like an adaptogen and reacts with your body for what you need in the moment. Diffuse while studying or during yoga or meditation for a grounding experience.
- Add a drop of Lemon, Frankincense, and Oregano or Thyme to an empty veggie capsule and take it three times a day with meals for immune support. Frankincense boosts immunity, multiplies white blood cells, helps cool chronic and low-grade systemic inflammation.
- Use Frankincense internally under the tongue, roof of your mouth, or in a veggie capsule for cellular and brain health support. Its antioxidant properties help in the fight against damaging free radicals.
- Google Frankincense and Cancer Support, Dr. Eric Zielinski, who specializes in public health research and aromatherapy for more education.
- Apply to your temples along with Peppermint and Lavender to calm headache pain. Here's a supporting headache rollerball you can make and keep on hand in your purse, car, office desk, gym bag, wherever- 7 drops of Peppermint, 7 drops of Lavender, 2 drops of Copaiba, 2 drops of Frankincense, and 2 drops of Wintergreen. Top off with carrier oil in a 10 ml rollerball.

Health Coaching Tip: Headaches are a good indication that the body is missing something, which could be either dehydration or nutrient deficiency. They can be triggered by food allergies, stress, fatigue, eyestrain, poor posture, alcohol or drugs, low blood sugar, hormones, or even constipation! First, try to consume more water, stretch out tense muscles, and/or apply a cold cloth like the peppermint ice bowl cloth to your forehead and around your neck. Making an eye doctor appointment and keeping a food journal to track possible allergens are good tips too.

Lavender:

- Rub a couple of drops onto the bottoms of your feet to calm your nerves before a dentist appointment, or to your pulse points to relax you during a stressful day.
- Add 15 drops of Lavender and distilled water to a 2 oz dark spray bottle and spritz down your yoga mat to freshen it up and mellow you out at the same time.
- Massage Lavender with a carrier oil or scent-free lotion over your sore joints and muscles to relieve the inflammation.
- Add a drop to your non-toxic skin care products to reduce the appearance of skin imperfections and soothe dry skin.
- Add a drop of Lavender, Peppermint, and Frankincense to Aloe Vera Gel and rub over sunburnt skin. Or, make a refreshing sunburnt skin spritzer with 10 drops of Lavender, 10 drops of Peppermint, distilled water in a 2 oz spray bottle. Lavender calms heat and itchiness while hydrating the skin.
- Add a drop to an itchy bug bite for quick relief-easy peasy!
- Diffuse 2 drops of Lemon with 2 drops of Lavender and Peppermint to settle allergy symptoms.

- Diffuse Lavender next to your bed to calm, relax and prepare your body and mind for a restful night's sleep, and/or rub onto the bottoms of your feet, back of the neck, or spine area.
- Using a 2 oz dark glass spray bottle, 10 drops of Lavender, 5 drops of either Vetiver, Cedarwood, Clary Sage or Roman Chamomile, and 1 ½ oz distilled water or witch hazel, spray this sleepy-time blend on your pillows or your bedding before settling in for the night. (4)

Health Coaching Tip: A poor nights' sleep, or many in a row, may be caused by stress and anxiety in our lives, too much coffee and stimulants, sugar, alcohol, pain, lack of physical activity, or moving our bodies, hormonal changes and more. Consider reducing the amount of caffeine that you drink after noon, incorporate yoga or slow stretching, or a guided meditation routine later in the evening to help you wind down from the day.

*Lemon:

- Add one drop to a drop of liquid Stevia or a bit of honey in a cup of warm water, and drink first thing in the morning before consuming anything else. This is a great way to "break your fast" and cleanse the digestive system to begin your day.
- Add a drop to your green smoothie or green juice for cleansing.
- Add a drop to a teaspoon of honey at the first sign of a sore throat and take it a few times a day, and/or dilute with a carrier oil and rub over a sore throat. Add a drop of Lemon, Frankincense, and Oregano or Thyme to an empty veggie capsule and take it for immune support. Lemon supports

lymphatic drainage and rids the body of impurities, mucus, and phlegm.

- Add a drop to the palm of your hands, rub together and take at least 3 long inhales, or diffuse for a pick-me-up and cheer-me-up, or to ward off germs too! Double duty! All citrus oils have these uplifting properties so you can also try Orange, Lime, Bergamot, and Grapefruit- pick your favourite.
- For you ladies waking up hot in the middle of the night or having hot flashes during the day, add 7 drops of Clary Sage, 5 drops of Geranium, 5 drops of Peppermint, and 4 drops of *Lemon to 1 ½ oz Witch Hazel in a 2 oz dark spray bottle. Shake and spritz on your neck and chest and anywhere you feel overheated. (5)
- Add 15 drops of Lemon, 15 drops of Eucalyptus, ¼ cup white vinegar and 1 ¾ cup distilled water to a 16 oz dark glass spray bottle to use as an all-purpose cleaner.
- Use directly to get sticky tags off the glass, sap off clothes, or gum out of hair.
- Add a couple of drops to a wet rag and place it in a load of laundry to freshen it up naturally.
- Add a drop or two to a piece of paper towel and place it at the bottom of your garbage bin under the bag to reduce odours.
- Diffuse a few drops of Lemon while cooking fish or hamburger meat to reduce the odours.
- Diffuse 2 drops of Lemon with 2 drops of Lavender and Peppermint to settle allergy symptoms. Lemon acts as a natural antihistamine.

Mama Tip: As soon as your allergies appear, start taking your outdoor clothes off when coming into the house. Leave them in the laundry room to keep the allergens from having free reign in your home, on your couches, and in your beds. Wear indoor clothes inside and outdoor clothes outside. I know that can be a pain in the butt, but it works! Always shower before going to bed at night, especially to keep those allergens from settling in your nasal cavity as you sleep at night. Adding a drop of Eucalyptus to a sponge in your nightly shower is even a better idea to open your sinuses.

Melaleuca (Tea Tree):

- Add a couple of drops of Melaleuca (Tea Tree) or Eucalyptus to your hair care products if the dreaded lice outbreak happens in your child's classroom.
- Use this rollerball recipe for overall immune support- 6 drops of Lemon, 4 drops of Melaleuca (Tea Tree), 4 drops of Oregano, 3 drops of Eucalyptus and 3 drops of Clove combined with fractionated coconut oil in a 10 ml rollerball (adult dilution). Apply to the bottoms of your feet, your pulse points, or back neck and spine 3-4 times a day when you start feeling under the weather.
- Rub a drop of diluted Melaleuca (Tea Tree) directly on your neck area at the first sign of a sore throat, or around the ear at the first sign of an earache. Remember that essential oils cannot go into eyes, ears, or the nose. Instead, try placing a drop of colloidal silver in your aching ear to help fight a brewing infection.
- Mix Melaleuca with Lemon and/or Oregano and distilled water in a spray bottle, then spray your shower and shower doors to prevent mold growth, or diffuse Melaleuca and Lemon on holidays in a tropical climate to reduce mold exposure.

- Use Melaleuca with Frankincense or Lavender to help cleanse a wound area, not applying it directly to the wound.
- Use 10 drops of Melaleuca (Tea Tree) with 2 ounces of witch hazel as a natural toner.
- Add a drop directly to a pimple a few times a day as soon as it first appears. If it's the large, under the skin kind that hurts, consider making a 10ml rollerball with 15 drops of Melaleuca (Tea Tree), 10 drops of Lavender, 5 drops of Rosemary, Geranium and Juniper Berry added to Jojoba oil, or carrier oil of your choice and apply a few times a day- This is an adult dilution.

Oregano:

- Apply a diluted drop or two to the bottoms of your feet as soon as you start feeling run down, then put on socks before you walk around the house. Its antibacterial properties are powerful enough to kill different kinds of bacteria and help protect the body from toxicity. It is ideal for immune support, acting as a natural antibiotic of sorts. Use this rollerball recipe for overall immune support- 6 drops of Lemon, 4 drops of Melaleuca (Tea Tree), 4 drops of Oregano, 3 drops of Eucalyptus and 3 drops of Clove combined with fractionated coconut oil in a 10 ml rollerball (adult dilution). Apply to the bottoms of your feet, your pulse points, or back neck and spine 3-4 times a day when you start feeling under the weather.
- Soak your feet in warm water with Epsom Salt and Oregano for 15-20 minutes.
- Add a drop of Lemon, Frankincense, and Oregano or Thyme to an empty veggie capsule and take it for immune support three times a day with

meals, for up to 10 days. This helps to fight against bacterial infections. Oregano can feel like it is burning your tummy if taken on an empty stomach, so I highly recommend taking the veggie capsule while consuming food. (*Do not rely on essential oils to replace the advice of a doctor, seek medical attention as necessary).

- Fight toenail fungus by applying diluted Oregano directly to the toenail.
- Combat yeast, like Candida, and parasites by adding 2-4 drops to a veggie capsule and take twice daily for up to 10 days with food.
- Drop carefully onto the tip of a wart, avoiding getting oregano directly on healthy surrounding skin because it may burn. Do this a couple of times a day until you see it begin to deaden.
- Mix Melaleuca with Oregano and distilled water in a spray bottle, spray your shower and shower doors to prevent mold growth.

Peppermint:

- Start your day with diffusing Peppermint and Wild Orange in your bedroom or kitchen as a fabulous way to energize you and your family in the morning.
- Dilute a couple of drops of peppermint with a carrier oil or unscented lotion and rub over sore joints and muscles for soothing relief.
- Add one drop of Peppermint to a drop of liquid Stevia or a tiny bit of honey in a cup of hot water to soothe digestive discomfort. Dilute Peppermint and Ginger with a carrier oil and rub over your stomach or on the bottom of your feet for nausea and motion sickness.
- Add a drop to your green smoothie or green juice for energy, or to a large stainless steel or glass

water bottle before a sporting event or workout for an energy boost.

- Add a drop to a bowl of ice water, soak a cloth in it, wring out the excess water, and then place it on your neck, chest, and under arms or between thighs to help reduce a fever.
- Apply to your temples along with Frankincense and Lavender to calm headache pain. It improves circulation and reduces pain.
- Diffuse in your vehicle to help you stay alert on long road trips or use a rollerball and apply diluted to your chest or back of your neck to wake you up.
- Add a drop to the palm of your hands, rub together and inhale, or diffuse with Wild Orange to help focus while studying or working on an important project. Add a couple of drops of Rosemary to the Peppermint in a diffuser to help support memory, Grapefruit and Peppermint for an uplifting vibe, or Peppermint and Sandalwood for grounding.
- Diffuse 2 drops with 2 drops of Lavender and Peppermint to settle allergy symptoms.
- Add 7 drops of Clary Sage, 5 drops of Geranium, 5 drops of Peppermint and 4 drops of Lemon to 1 ½ oz Witch Hazel in a 2 oz dark spray bottle. Shake and spritz on your neck and chest and anywhere you feel overheated. (5)
- Add a drop of Lavender, Peppermint, and Frankincense to Aloe Vera Gel and rub over burnt sunburnt skin.
- Dilute 10 drops of Peppermint with 5 drops of Lemongrass and ¾ cup distilled water in a 2 oz dark glass spray bottle, spray around your windows and doors and along your baseboards to repel insects in your homes, RVs, and tents. (6)
- Add a couple of drops of Peppermint and/or Eucalyptus to a sponge during your shower to open

your airways and relieve congestion. You can also add a drop of Peppermint/Eucalyptus to a bowl of hot water and tent yourself over it, opening your airways. Diffuse Peppermint/Eucalyptus next to your bed to help you breathe better while you sleep.

Health Coaching Tip: To help flush out the irritants, start sinus washing with a Neti-pot as soon as you start feeling congested.

Rosemary:

- Add a drop to your shampoo or conditioner to strengthen your hair and support hair growth.
- Add to soups and vegetable dishes for an amazing flavour. I add a little Rosemary and maple syrup to steamed carrots, yummy!
- Diffuse Rosemary during the day with Peppermint, Wild Orange, and/or Frankincense to stimulate focus and memory.
- Add one to two drops in a veggie capsule and take daily to balance hormones and blood sugar levels, and to support detoxification.
- Mix 2 drops of Rosemary with 2 drops of Peppermint and carrier oil of your choice to cool inflammation from sore muscles and joints. It acts as a natural analgesic.
- Dilute and apply topically with Eucalyptus and/or Peppermint to your chest to thin and expel mucus.

*Wild Orange:

- Add one drop to a drop of liquid Stevia or a bit of honey and water or tea to boost the immune system with its virus and bacteria-fighting abilities and cancer-fighting d-limonene, which defends against oxidative stress.

- Add a drop to your green smoothie or green juice for cleansing and detoxifying.
- Apply 2-3 drops to your abdominal area to boost digestion and to ease cramps and constipation.
- Add 10 drops of Eucalyptus, Peppermint, and Wild Orange to ¼ cup white vinegar and 1 ¾ cup distilled water in a 16 oz dark glass spray bottle. Use as an all-purpose cleaner on your countertops, appliances, showers, toilets, sinks, door handles, and light switches. Great way to keep the germs at bay while smelling up your house with a refreshing and non-toxic scent.
- Add a drop to Avocado Oil to make a light and refreshing salad dressing.
- Diffuse with Frankincense and Peppermint to help with focus and motivation.
- Give yourself a giant, squishy hug with Wild Orange, or as I like to call it, my sunshine oil! All citrus oils have uplifting properties to cheer you up or calm you down, reducing the effects of stress. You can also try *Lemon, *Lime, *Bergamot, and *Grapefruit. Bergamot and Wild Orange to release negative emotions and encourage happy thoughts! Try using these oils in these various ways for stress relief, but keep in mind citrus oils are photosensitive and should not be applied on your skin before going out into the sun.

- Massage onto the base of the skull
- Rub on the inside of the elbow
- Use an essential oil diffuser
- Apply a drop to the palms and inhale
- Rub into the wrists and carry the aroma with you all day

**In no way are essential oils a replacement for professional treatment of mental illness or symptoms of anxiety and depression. Think of them as a tool to support your journey to wellness. A one-time usage may not alter your mood, so be consistent. Try using small amounts on a more regular basis. Remember too, that we are all unique and essential oils can affect one person differently than another. Try closing your eyes while smelling different oils. The ones that you are drawn to most are usually the ones you need now. Trust your gut.

Health Coaching Tip: Much of our mood and emotions percolate from what's brewing in our digestive system. Consider checking in on your gut health when working through anxiety.

Well, my friends, that's a wrap! I hope you found a nugget or two within these pages that has inspired you to swap out some non-toxic products in your home for cleaner and safer solutions. Essential Oils are truly gifts from the earth as plant-based alternatives to healthier living.

If you have any questions at all, I would love to hear from you. Shoot me an email through my website, Karen's Pure Balance. I offer FREE one-hour introductory wellness sessions and would love to support you along your wellness journey.

Love Yourself, Live Pure.
Karen

Action Step:

Do you use essential oils? Which ones stood out to you that you may want to include into your life?

Frankincense – The King of Oils Indeed!

"People who don't use oils, make no Frankin' cense."

~ Unknown

Frankincense is the king of all oils! I remember this oil distinctively because, in the Certified Holistic Cancer Practitioners (CHCP) course, I remember writing down the phrase *"crosses the blood-brain barrier."* I knew that it was extremely beneficial for those going through a brain cancer diagnosis because of this extraordinary feature. This amazing oil reduces brain swelling. I began pouring a couple of drops into the palm of my hand, dipping the fingerprint side of my thumb into the oil, and placing it at the roof of my mouth. This would get directly to my brain faster and its antioxidant benefits affected my entire body, including my brain. I would rub what was left into my wrists and onto the back of my neck.

It has so many amazing antioxidant superpowers that this is something I will continue to take in the future. I do believe that this one oil, combined with the whole food product I was taking, brought my antioxidant levels to well above normal range when tested, even during chemo when they would normally have been low. Seeing this was an amazing surprise. This powerful essential oil is incredible for any type of cancer.

I was using a few other rollerballs that Karen put together for me. Adrenals, Serenity oil, Hope, Empowerment, and Focus. Also, Clary Calm, which I put on my abdomen once a month for those fun PMS cramps. That saved me from taking medication- loved them all!

Action Step:

What oils do you use in your daily routines? Is there one special oil that you can't live without? Maybe this is something that you can investigate further.

Move Your Body

"I can tell you that what you are looking for is already inside YOU!"

~ Anne Lamott

Studies have shown that those who exercise five days a week or more get sick less than those who don't exercise. If they did get sick, it wouldn't last as long. I have never regretted going for a workout when I didn't feel like going in the first place. It does the body good!

Studies show that at least three days a week of exercise is beneficial to the body. It gets your heart rate up and gets your circulation moving. Simply walking is still good for the body as well. Soak up some sunshine and vitamin D, get outside, and take time to smell the tulips!

Benefits of Exercise:

- More energy
- Keeps your muscles and joints flexible and strong
- Boosts your mood and self-esteem
- Gives your brain a boost
- Lowers cholesterol, strengthens the heart
- Helps the thyroid gland function optimally
- Strengthens your immune system and lungs

- Reduces your risk of Type 2 Diabetes
- Sleep better
- Strengthens bones
- Keeps you feeling and looking young
- Reduces your risk of cancer!

"Those who think they have no time for bodily exercise will sooner or later have to find time for illness."

~ Edward Stanley

Examples of Exercise:

- Walking
- Jogging
- Yoga
- Dancing
- Martial Arts
- Kickboxing
- Sports like tennis, soccer, baseball, etc.
- Bike Riding
- Go to the Gym- cardio machines
- Swimming
- Rebounding

What is Rebounding?

A rebounder is like a mini trampoline. Most come with handles so you can hang on to the railing if needed. You can use the rebounder to gently bounce up and down to get your lymphatic system moving. The lymphatic system is like a garbage disposal. The only way to cleanse it is by getting the body moving. Jumping up and down on the rebounder is a great way to get your entire lymphatic system moving and detoxifying. I learned about this when I was diagnosed with lymphoma and was using a rebounder throughout that process until I had to give it up when my basement flooded.

A simple ten minutes of exercise a day does your body good!

Benefits:

- Detoxification
- Exercise
- Cellulite Reduction
- Bone and joint-friendly
- Helps circulate the blood
- Helps support your immune system

Action Step:

What do you do for exercise? Have you tried a rebounder? Make a list of what you enjoy doing because we both know that, if you don't enjoy it, you're not going to do it.

Earthing – Soaking Up Mother Nature

"Take a quiet walk with mother nature. It will nurture your mind, body, and soul."

~ A. D. Williams

Have you heard of Earthing or Grounding before? This is the process of getting up close and personal with Mother Nature. I'm talking about being barefoot right on the grass! This process of getting connected is beneficial for our bodies. I admit that I didn't do Earthing the first six months of the year because I live in Edmonton and, when the snow hits the ground in October, it's there until at least April. Once the grass was visible again, I was taking off my socks and digging my feet right in there!

Earthing may have healing abilities, too. The electrons that the Earth gives off are beneficial to our bodies. It can help us fight off free radicals aka the bad guys that can cause cancer. Studies have shown that grounding reduced the amount of stress, fatigue, depression, and pain in the participants. Twenty minutes of it may even reduce symptoms of jet lag and PMS! It also can help remove EMF radiation from your body. All of this is a great reason to get dirty.

Water and sand can also produce these same healing effects. You can buy grounding blankets that also have this capability. I have never tried one; however, this is something that I'm considering trying, especially in the winter.

Action Step:

Next time you go for a walk and pass a lush green grass area, take your socks off and soak the electrons up! Doesn't that feel good!

Principle of Healing III

No More Dirt! Detoxify Your Life and Heal Your Spirit

Forgiveness, Emotional Freedom Technique, Soul Retrieval...

Diving Into a Few Things that have a Deeper Connection Inside of Us

Multi-dimensional Healing Love Force
Christina Vignal

"Always sleep with open hands, it keeps the energy flowing."

~ Christina Vignal

One thing I've come to know is that powerful healing is available on all levels and there is a network of support offering natural empowering tools and modalities. When offering an opportunity for the body to feel seen, heard, and noticed, a world of possibility opens for healing to occur. It's a beautiful piece of someone's journey to be a part of.

I am so incredibly honoured to have been part of the LOVE FORCE that worked with and supported Tanya, helping her to strengthen her vital thriving foundation and be an assistant in reminding her cells and essence that they are loved, seen, heard, held, healthy, and strong.

My name is Christina Vignal, and I am a registered massage therapist. I use the modalities of massage therapy, CranioSacral therapy, and lymphatic drainage with my clients, offering a safe space and the possibility for transformation and healing activation to occur. Along my twenty-one-year journey as a therapist and practitioner, my techniques have expanded and evolved along with my knowledge and curiosity. I have so much gratitude as it continues to be an amazing, rewarding service to offer.

As I sat and ponder in the curiosity of how I might go about writing the chapter of a book, these questions presented themselves:

Purpose/why? Remember the purpose, the intent that leads to the next best step.

My purpose? This one was easy– to be a vessel of love and healing for Tanya's physical, mental, spiritual, and energetic bodies by offering grounding calmness, safe container, and bodywork modalities.

What is possible when offering love, touch, and care with a sacred reverence for another or oneself?

Might healing potential be expanded?

Might relaxation, rest, and positive processing be enabled and activated with more ease, grace, and compassion?

As a sacred self-care practice when some is offering to themselves, does it open the experience of self-holding, nurturing, and loving self?

What does this heal? Activate?

I continue to ask these questions while curiously creating possibilities for healing, activation, and transformation.

Add specific modalities and techniques to an experience. These can be massage therapy, CranioSacral therapy, and lymphatic drainage, which are known for these benefits and more:

- Encouraging parasympathetic response
- Improving tissue healing

- Reducing muscle tension
- Increasing joint mobility and flexibility
- Improving circulation
- Decreasing scarring post-surgery or injury
- Reducing stress hormones
- Increasing relaxation
- Increasing fluid movement in the right direction
- Reducing swelling
- Improving skin tone
- Strengthening the immune system
- Increasing energy
- Improving sleep
- Reduces heart rate
- Lowers blood pressure

Now, what's possible?

I am recognizing the value and importance of going back to, what I'm recognizing now, was the beginning... back to when I began to develop knowledge about healing the body with touch.

As a teenager, my family had a hairdresser who we used to go and see at her house. During one of our appointments, the hairdresser was talking with my mom about my Mom's headaches and asked me to come over and watch what she was doing with her hands and then copy her. I watched her hold her hands over my mom's head, and raise them a little, put them down, then raise them again, and then move them away. She turned to me and said, "*Okay... you try.*" I moved over towards my mom and put my hands over her head. The hairdresser asked, "*Do you feel that? Do you feel anything?*" I recall looking at her and thinking, "Feel anything like what?" and she said, "Anything hot or cold, bubbly or tingly." At that moment, I recognized I did feel something. I felt a tingling sensation under my hands and, when I moved my hands, the sensations changed. It was a little hotter, more tingly, more intense, or colder. When I experienced my hands feeling a strong, powerful, more amplified sensation, the hairdresser directed me to move my hands higher up into the air, farther away from my Mom's head, and pull that feeling away as I lifted my hands and then let the feelings go. After repeating this a few times, Mom's headache was gone. I recall occasionally doing this for my mom at home and it provided her relief. "Very interesting," I thought to myself.

Looking back at that situation now while understanding a lot more about energy, I know the expansion of possibilities that are available when incorporating that awareness into everything that I do. It is part of the medicine that has been very helpful as a practitioner and for myself.

Following that experience, I had many more experiences that seemed kind of odd and cool at the same time. People would find me at school and ask me to work on them. I told my friends about the situation that happened with my mom at the hairdresser's. In all honesty, knowing myself from back then, I would have been a little arrogant about how 'I' did this 'thing' my hairdresser taught me. At the same time, it worked and was amazing. Friends who had sore shoulders, necks, knees, or a headache or who had gotten injured doing something in the gym or while playing their sport, would find me and I would "pull the energy out," or do some massage, and 99% of the time it worked!

During that same time, I was a competitive volleyball player for my school and city teams. As an active teen, I had knee and low back pain. I received a few treatments from a friend's mom, who was a massage therapist. I recall the relaxation and relief that came after each treatment. I quickly understood massage therapy as a helpful, healing modality. Little did I know that this period of my life was offering me my first playground experience as a practitioner.

Our teams took long bus rides driving to tournaments all over British Columbia and I would massage my teammates for six of the eight hours while we were riding the bus.

As a late teen/young adult with all the thoughts and feelings, I desired to fit in, be liked, and be important because of being the one on the bus who would massage everyone. This created some of those feelings for me while I was helping my friends and teammates at the same time.

At the end of my second year of college, where I was working towards becoming a Phys Ed teacher, I had the honest recognition that I had no desire to be a Phys Ed teacher. I took a break from post-secondary education to listen more deeply to what I wanted. The two years that I had studied in the Phys Ed program had been a valuable experience. I gained great knowledge of the human body, how it functions, and how it develops among other things. I then went on to work different jobs, uncertain as to what I wanted to do as a career. I became aware that maybe being a massage therapist was the thing for me. I ended up moving to Calgary and took the 2,200-hour massage therapy program offered at the Foothills College of Massage Therapy.

I enjoyed the school and the program. I felt like my hands already knew what to do and enjoyed expanding my understanding of the body. Helping people to heal and feel better after an injury, or dealing with areas of tension or discomfort, and being able to be part of what helped that to unravel or go away was validating and gratifying. There was also an element of personal pressure that I had applied to myself, feeling that in some way it was 'me' doing it. It was my responsibility when someone came in with a complaint about a certain issue. By the end of their one-hour massage, that thing that they were complaining about should be totally healed, totally gone. Little did I know that, in many ways, the opposite would be true.

I felt divinely blessed on my first job as a massage therapist in a chiropractic office. While in massage school, I had my first experience with being adjusted after misaligning my elbow. It was a profound learning experience for me to receive chiropractic care. My expanded learning continued when I worked in conjunction with a chiropractor for my six-month case study at the end of massage school. The combination of massage, chiropractic, and yoga offered a life-altering physical realignment for the twenty-five-year-old client we were working with. After finishing that study, I was intent on working in conjunction with two specific chiropractors.

The clinic I worked in had two chiropractors and three receptionists- all women. Each of them had a wealth of knowledge in different areas. I learned so much and am extremely grateful for the many ways they helped to expand my context of understanding how the body works, how energy works, and how energy moved or was held in areas where possible complaints and discomfort originated. They introduced me to the work of Louise Hay along with many other modalities of natural medicine, natural body work, complementary tools for holistic care, and a completely different understanding of what was possible for myself and the people I was working with. The concept that physical complaints or discomfort had a connection to psychological, emotional, and energetic components was fascinating and expanding for me.

I can still remember a very pivotal moment working at the chiropractic office. I worked with a man who had come in complaining of an incredibly sore back and I did my best to offer him a massage that would be very healing for him. We had a deep conversation about his life and previous injury. He left the office feeling grateful for his treatment. At home that night, I sat down on the living room to eat my dinner and relax. Attempting to get up, my back was so piercingly sore that I couldn't stand up. I crawled up the stairs to bed. I was incredibly thankful to wake up feeling more mobile and having less discomfort. Thank goodness I worked at a chiropractic office with an incredibly wonderful and skilled chiropractor. She was able to help me out with an adjustment and some muscle work. She also brought to my awareness the importance of being grounded while working with clients, a concept I hadn't heard of before. After being treated, I received a phone call from the client who I had worked with the previous day. He was in tears because he felt so amazing! He had no back pain at all! This was a new experience for him because he had been dealing with constant back pain for fifteen years before that morning. I found this incredibly informative and incredibly amazing. It was a representation of what was, and what is, available in possibility. This was also a powerful experience of what's possible when the intention is to truly help someone to heal and when they intend to heal.

Another important element in my learning was through receiving treatments of all different holistic healing modalities, massage therapy, CranioSacral therapy, lymphatic drainage, acupuncture, SRT, SIT, biofeedback, hypnotherapy, chiropractic care, spa facials, working with naturopathic doctors, iridologists, homeopathic doctors. In each of my experiences, there were opportunities for me to learn through physical touch, energetic perception, and my responses. I found that the interaction and the style of each offering affected my system's ability to digest what was being offered. This greatly expanded my sensitivity and awareness to how I was showing up for others and how I was creating a space to welcome them. I recall some treatments being offered with great sensitivity, care, and tenderness, comparative to others where I perceived a higher level of aggressive, forceful, or intense offering.

I felt an interesting contrast in my personal experience as the receiver of treatment. One style of treatment was comparative to another, bringing about a new curiosity. What would be the experience with clients who came in with the expectation that working with a particular discomfort or complaint would require an aggressive forceful process? Instead, could I offer them an invitation to sink further into themselves into space and whatever might be there? This intrigue has opened so many possibilities. From a foundation of nurturing tender care and patience, I have experienced and witnessed so many people unravel in a very loving, graceful, surrender in areas that had been holding extreme discomfort or long-held tension. That has been beautiful, transformative work. This work has shaped the last five years of what I am now understanding was a transition from an old-style to now creating an invitation for the body. I have found that so much more transformative and available.

Along the way, I have been part of and witnessed many beautiful examples of the incredible healing that is available. Having worked with newborns, children, teenagers, and adults up to 100-years-old, the availability of healing and transformation is always there.

I've also taken opportunities to expand my skill set learning the techniques of CranioSacral therapy (Level 1, 2, & SER 1) and Manual Lymphatic Drainage (Level 1 & 2).

Along with the expansion of the technical skills I learned expanded methods of perceiving what the system wanted to share or was possibly resisting sharing, each offered many new tools to utilize. Having practiced as a massage therapist for twenty-one years now, I have come to a new level of understanding.

I am only part of the process for whoever comes to work with me.

The techniques I utilize are part of the process.
The environment is part of the process.
The conversation is part of the process.
The beliefs, perceptions, and willingness of the client are
huge part of the process.

This past year, working as a massage therapist with clientele who have been living a very different year of their life than they have ever before, has broadened my scope of practice.

In September, an awareness dropped that the bodies that were on the massage table were bodies that were craving to be held, nourished, nurtured, and seen. In my context of thought that all points to being loved. I began a new experiment. What if the core of what I was offering came from the essence of love as an offering to each cell of the body? "You are seen," "You are heard," "You are important," "Thank you for what you're doing." It has been an absolute gift to be a part of and to be witness to the beautiful transformation that has occurred for people.

My curiosity, intrigue, and knowledge in working with the fluid system, the lymphatic system of the body, has increased. Being more aware of the lymphatic system and encouraging its healthy flow presents an opportunity for a huge impact on the whole body, I was very curious to begin treatment with Tanya with that being a focus.

This brings me to my experience working with Tanya. After considering and eliminating the concern of any possible contraindications for Tanya, we began treatment. Our first connection was via Zoom and this was my first experience working with someone long-distance. I found it very powerful as the ability to perceive energetically and physically some of what Tanya's system was experiencing was very powerful and allowed a treatment that produced relaxation and increased Tanya's comfort.

Beginning in February, Tanya was able to come to my studio, where we began biweekly treatments. She had been experiencing feelings of incredible pressure in her head, face, and neck along with tension, lack of mobility in her jaw, buzzing in her ears, anxiety, and difficulty sleeping. The focus of our treatment was to decrease swelling and scar tissue and increase flexibility and overall comfort. This was all peacefully, comfortably abled with lymphatic drainage, CranioSacral therapy, and massage.

By the end of the treatment, there was a visible decrease in swelling on Tanya's head, face, and neck. She shared that she was experiencing a significant decrease in the feeling of pressure and tension throughout her head, face, and neck. She appeared calmer and more relaxed. As she left, I asked myself, "How differently was Tanya going to experience her evening?" Up until this point, she had been having great difficulty in achieving a solid or restful sleep and knowing the value of healing that's available while we sleep. I was curious to know if this would be a response for Tanya's system. She connected with me the next day to let me know that she had had a very peaceful and solid sleep and was feeling clearer and lighter.

It was following our second in-person session that Tanya connected with me once again to share that the treatment had been very impactful. She asked if there was anything available that she could do herself in between treatments with me. After doing a bit of research, I came across a publication from UHN, The University Health Network of Toronto, a network made up of Toronto General, Toronto Western, Princess Margaret, Toronto Rehab, and Michener Institute. It was a step-by-step instruction document on how to do Lymphatic Self Massage on your face, head, and neck. The publication was for patients of Princess Margaret Cancer Center who were treated for head and neck cancer with surgery to remove a tumour or lymph node or with radiation therapy. I was so incredibly grateful to have come across a very detailed and easily understandable publication with step-by-step instructions of how an individual could go about offering themselves treatment. In all honesty, I was completely shocked that Tanya had not been offered something like this as part of her post-surgery recovery plan. Both Tanya and I were very intrigued, curious, and excited about the possibilities of offering this type of treatment to her body every day. What potential impact and possibility might this create? I met Tanya at her place and spent time in conversation with her about the document and about the practice itself.

Tanya's next appointment with me was six days following that. Greeting her at the front door, I recognized a visible decrease in the swelling and inflammation on her head, face, and neck. There was also a visible decrease in puckering around her scar. Most evident was a general sense of happiness, vitality, rejuvenation in Tanya's expression. It was fascinating to work on her that day. In my experience, her body was at another level of willingness to receive, to let go, and to unwind.

Moving forward, each time I saw Tanya, I experienced another level of vitality in rejuvenation in her essence, her being, how her body felt, and how it responded to the offering of each treatment. I felt so inspired by Tanya's willingness and determination and the effort that she put in choosing how she was walking through her journey. In my experience, she allowed herself to be supported in the direction of her highest good on all levels- physically, mentally, emotionally, and spiritually and it was a beautiful experience to witness the power of possibility created by her choices.

In witnessing the impact of Tanya's daily self-lymphatic massage work, I was intrigued as to how much of an impact the physical process of the techniques had as well as the impact of what I witnessed was daily sacred self-care! I experienced her recollection of her daily treatments with love and softness and gratitude. I came to understand that the process of creating space and time to honour oneself in a way that is nourishing, and nurturing creates exponential possibilities in what's available in healing.

I feel deep reverence, honour, and gratitude for having been a participant and witness to Tanya's journey. And to the journey of all those I work with.

Thank you. Thank you. Thank you.

Action Step:

Have you done massage therapy yourself? It is a great way to improve your body and get the relief your body needs! Notice the difference with frequency, depending on what your body could use to heal.

Stress Management

"Life is tough my darling, but so are you."

~ Stephanie Bennet Henry
~ Joanna's favourite quote

Stress can come in any form in our lives, but when it becomes a version of chronic stress, that's when it takes a toll on our health and our immune system. Trust me, I know this all too well.

If you want a strong immune system, you need to learn how to handle and manage the stress in your life. I know too many people who live in stressful jobs every day. They are unhappy with their job and stay way too long in an unhealthy environment.

If you aren't happy where you are... change it!
Not happy with the people around you... change it!

Find a stress management tool that works for YOU and start using it. Staying unhappy, dealing with negative people around you WILL lead to dis-ease within our bodies. Stress can't be avoided; we can however learn to manage it... or change it.

There are other stressors that happen in our lives that we begin to stress over and over again. It consumes our minds. It might be time to find a way out and let it go.

The key is to realize that every single person is different and not everything will work for everybody, and we can ALL do something to improve our health. Everybody. Period.

Everyone has to deal with stress on some level in their lives. It can come from work, family, health, relationships, finances, etc. The problem is, if we don't know how to handle the stress when it comes our way, eventually it turns into a snowball that just keeps growing to the point where we feel like we are ALWAYS under stress and that isn't healthy for our body. We need to stop this snowball effect!

Now, some stress can be good. For example, when we are exercising, that is short-term stress that can be good for the body and the brain. Nobody lives their life in a flatline_____. We all have our ups and downs and, when we are in a down, we need to know how to get back up. Staying down there for a prolonged period causes bad things to happen to your health.

Some things that happen are those we start to self-medicate. We don't realize we are doing it, but a lot of people when under stress eat, take drugs, drink, watch a lot of TV or become workaholics. We DON'T want this to happen. We want to make "healthy" choices as ways to manage our stress.

Some easy tips you can do to handle stress are:

- Stop procrastinating – Do the task that is always at the bottom of your list first. You will feel better getting this task out of the way.
- Just say NO – We have to realize that we can't do it all! At some point, we need to say, "NO, I can't do that," or just simply say NO.
- Talk about it – It is okay to reach out to a friend or seek counselling from a professional. Keeping everything bottled up inside is a recipe for disaster. Talk it out. I could preach about this one. Let those emotions out!

The BIG THREE:

1. Write it out – A lot of people are journaling, and it does work. If you aren't journaling with this book, what are you waiting for? Write out everything that is bothering you and even if NO ONE else reads it, you will feel better.

2. Forgiveness – Sometimes we feel like we will never forgive that person or we can't forgive ourselves for something we might have done. This isn't something that you want to carry with you. Make a list of everyone that you want to forgive or that you want to ask forgiveness from and just do it. Even if they don't forgive you, you said what you needed to say and now you CAN let it go. Forgive those that you are holding a grudge or grievance with. Genuinely forgive them because *"Resentment is like drinking poison every day and expecting the other person to die"* ~ Carrie Fisher.

3. Be Thankful – Make a list of everything you are thankful for each day– your family, your kids, the roof over your head, or even that avocados were on sale at the grocery store. Sell something for $10? Give thanks for the $10. This will naturally raise your vibration and give you a list to read when feeling stressed.

There are many more ways such as, Yoga, Meditation, deep breathing, Reiki, and reflexology. Exercise is an amazing stress reliever. Find something that works for you and go with that. Not everything will work for everybody, but you will find something that resonates with you.

Fun and Easy Ways to Reduce Stress:

1. Doodle Books – yes, those adult colouring books.
2. Dance like a kid again with no cares in the world.
3. Do something you love or try something new
4. Take a bath and don't forget your Epsom salts, especially nice right before bed.
5. Listen to a quiet meditation
6. Try deep breathing exercises– deeply inhale and hold, then breathe out all the air.
7. Pet an animal or cuddle your kid, nieces and nephew works for me.
8. Yoga
9. Laugh! Watch something funny or just start laughing – trust me, it works.
10. Exercise
11. Try aromatherapy– lavender is great for relaxing
12. Take a short nap
13. Soak in a cup of green tea
14. Drink more water! Again, stay hydrated!
15. Get enough sleep

Action Step:

Choose at least 5 things from this list and start to incorporate them into your daily or weekly routine. I learned the hard way that STRESS and not enough self-care can make a big impact on your life – and not in a good way.

Acupuncture

"Acupuncturist - not a magician but I understand your confusion."

~ Unknown

Acupuncture is the process of inserting very thin needles into specific points of the skin to help bring balance to your Chi, or life force. During my radiation, I had a few Acupuncture sessions to help lower the stress and anxiety levels that I was experiencing. It did help! Acupuncture can be used for so many things. Ask the person you know who performs this modality. It truly is a wonder that we're not using it often enough. If something is going on in your life and you're not sure who can help, this is a great time to call and ask questions and find out if this is the right option for you.

Acupuncture is known to reduce discomfort for the following issues:

- Chemotherapy-induced and postoperative nausea and vomiting
- Dental pain
- Headaches, including tension headaches and migraines
- Labor pain

- Low back pain
- Neck pain
- Osteoarthritis
- Menstrual cramps
- Respiratory disorders, such as allergic rhinitis

Action Step:

For someone who does not enjoy getting needles and has never seen one puncture my skin, this is not as scary as it may sound. I survived and I know that you will too. Give it a try for yourself and see what you think.

Infrared Sauna

"Sweat cleanses the body from the inside. It comes from places a shower will never reach."

~ George Sheehan

In my old house, I had an infrared sauna and I loved it and I miss it so much! I got one just after my cancer treatments when I was thirty years old. Sweating the toxins out of my body felt amazing. I was instantly energized and always felt great after having a shower to wash away the toxins.

When I sold my house in Ontario, I had to say goodbye to it- insert crying face here. I couldn't use one this round, but I know that I will be getting another one as soon as I can.

A near-infrared sauna uses heat and light to heat the body, getting deep into your tissues and helps sweat the toxins out. It barely uses any electricity, and it does not heat the area around it, so it is safe to have in your home. I highly recommend having one. If you can't get one for your home, a lot of spas offer this service.

Here are some of the benefits of an infrared sauna:

- Detoxification
- Anti-aging
- Pain reduction
- Joint and muscle support

- Cardiovascular support
- Boost metabolism
- Anti-inflammatory
- De-stressing YOU

It does wonders for the body. A session should last fifteen to twenty minutes. If you have never done it before, you may want to start with five minutes and work your way up to those fifteen to twenty minutes.

Follow the instructions from your health practitioner or from the company you purchased it from. Enjoy!

Action Step:

Always remember to rehydrate and drink lots of water afterward! In case I haven't mentioned drinking water enough, you are going to be sweating a lot. If you are not able to get one in your home, see if there is a location near you that offers this service. Give it a try and see what you think.

Forgiveness – Release Your Past! Let it Go!

"Forgiveness is not about letting someone off the hook for their actions, but freeing ourselves of negative energies that bind us to them."

~ Unknown

During this healing period of my life, I had a breakthrough. When I mentioned cleaning out the dustpan, I meant it! If you haven't seen the movie "Soul", you may want to check it out as it could help this make more sense. For the past fifteen years, I've had the same dream about my one ex-boyfriend now and then. He was not very kind to me, and I will just leave it there. What I realized was that, after years of counselling and journaling and writing letters where I said "I forgive you," in my heart... I didn't mean it. There was still some bitterness and resentment there. The dream I had was always the same- different locations, but always the same story. I was still in the home we had together and he was either upset with me for still being there or somewhere in the background of the dream wandering around. In frustration, I always thought to myself, "Why am I still here? I don't want to be here!" I would go around the house trying to collect my things and get out. The dream was on repeat... until last week.

Suddenly, I had a new dream and, this time, the theme changed. I had just woken up and was going to have a shower. I was going to different bathrooms in this giant

159

house and, finally, I found one in the basement. I noticed all my soaps and shampoos were already there and I thought to myself, "How nice it was that he had brought them there." That's when I felt it – a feeling of gratitude. He had done something thoughtful for me that made me smile. I got out of the shower and saw him sitting on the floor in the other room, mumbling something repeatedly. It was cold in that room, so I sprayed him with some warm water to warm him up and that's when I felt a tug of war inside me. Then another feeling hit me – **a feeling of GENUINE forgiveness.** I could feel my heart and my head saying, "Are you sure? Yes." I felt a wave of forgiveness wash over me and fill me up. Then I woke up and thought, "I'm going to be okay."

I got up, had my breakfast, sat down to do a healing meditation, and then started to cry. It overtook me. Something I didn't even realize was still inside me had been weighing me down all this time. Forgiveness, genuine forgiveness, was an overwhelmingly powerful experience. I followed this with some karmic cord-cutting. This is where you would close your eyes and pull the bad from inside of you like a ball of string, pulling until there was no more left. Cutting each strand that came from you so it was no longer connected. I ended up changing this ball of what was now pure light and pushed it back into me, keeping only the good and I was finally able to let go of the bad. At that moment, my breath started to change. It was such a powerful and transformational moment in my life. I talked to my friend Rae-ann afterward and told her that I had had a breakthrough in my dreams. She mentioned to me that he was most likely like one of the Soul monsters from the movie "Soul" who was stuck and unable to move on. I hope that our cord has now been released and our ties have been severed. He's now free to move on and so am I. To this day, I have not had that dream since. I am so thankful to be and feel free to move forward with my life.

We hold onto so many things that happened in our past. We've carried with us for so many years– for way too long. Living in your past keeps you in your past and, honestly, the best place to be is in the present day. I kept hearing that repeatedly and I truly understand that living in today, in this current moment, stops you from thinking about the what-ifs, what could be, and what could happen. Work with someone you trust and let that past go! Be free, feel free, and move forward with your incredible future.

Action Step:

There are two steps to forgiveness– forgiving others and forgiving yourself. I will discuss forgiving yourself in the next chapter. For now, write down a list of who/what you may still need to let go of, even though it might be tough.

Self-Muscle Testing

"Most people have no idea how good their body is designed to feel."

~ Kevin Trudeau

Throughout this book, I have mentioned frequencies and that everything has its own frequency, whether it be the supplements that were taken, food that was eaten, or products that we are using. We even have our frequencies. For example, being around someone who is extremely negative all the time, you can feel all their energy coming from them and it is not good energy to be around. The opposite is true of someone who is positive and is radiating positive energy. This is someone that we want to be around because their frequency/energy makes us feel good. Our bodies are in a healthy state when we are around a positive frequency. This is where the magic happens! When our frequency is vibrating at this higher more positive frequency, we want good vibes only.

One way to raise our vibrations is to test what we are fuelling our bodies with. If you want to know if something is good or bad for your specific body, try self-muscle testing. There is a lot of controversy around this topic. Some find it works and some find it inaccurate. I found that, when I used it, it could be a powerful tool to identify my body's needs.

Self-muscle testing is tapping into your subconscious mind. We discussed the power of our subconscious mind- it does know everything. Every single detail of our entire life is stored there. Your body knows what is good for it and what is not. For this process, I found the most accurate self-test to be the Two Hands Muscle Test.

How to do The Two Hands Muscle Test

Have your pinky and your thumb on one hand pressed together, creating an "O" shape and use the index finger, on the other hand, to try to break them apart. If they do break apart easily, this is a no response and, if they remain strong, this is a yes response. Be sure to use light resistance and not force your fingers to lock into position.

With any self-muscle test, you want to create a baseline reading first. Whichever method that you choose and is easy for you to get an accurate reading is the best one for you. You want to always start with a yes question or no question. For example, ask your body what your name is and give a positive answer. Then, test the same question, giving a negative answer. You can also use something that you can't predict like the word love or the word hate as these words carry their vibrational frequencies too. Love should give you a "yes" response and "hate" should give you a "no" response. In the beginning, you may need to do this test a few times until you get used to how your body will respond to asking it questions. If you are not getting an accurate response, you could be tired. Drinking a glass of water could be beneficial to you getting a more accurate reading.

To test a supplement or product, focus on that supplement in front of you and ask if it is good for YOUR body? You should receive a yes or no response.

Keep in mind that there are many other ways available to self-test or have someone else muscle test you as well. I found this technique did work for me or when it came to foods especially because my body would let me know any way that it was not good for me. Did I mention the tomatoes?

If you find you're not getting an accurate reading doing self muscle testing, you can find someone who knows how to muscle test on you, or you can move forward with the Emotional Freedom Technique, which will also help give you some answers about your body.

Action Step:

Have you tried self-muscle testing? Give the finger testing method a try and see if it works for you.

Emotional Freedom Technique (EFT)

"Shine like you were meant to shine!"

~ Unknown

When I first got out of the hospital and had a few weeks before starting my radiation and chemotherapy treatments, I was able to talk to Melissa. I had a lot of anxiety about the current situation and everything that had happened. An Emotional Freedom Technique session with her was offered and she asked me what I wanted to discuss with her. **I mentioned FEAR.** This was my most pressing feeling and how I felt about things going forward. She wanted to help me work through it. What I learned through working with her was that the "what if's" I kept thinking about and all the not great possibilities I could think of, didn't matter. That was the wrong mindset to have. I had to focus on the present moment and what was real right now. My feet are on the floor today. I'm sitting at my desk and I'm alive. She suggested that I list three things that I heard, two things that I smelled, and one thing that I could taste. This would help ground me into the current moment and settle my anxiety.

I've heard this from more than one person before- being in the present moment is the best mental place that you can be. Thinking about all the possibilities that could go wrong in your future is not a great place. Today, you are okay. Today, you are alive. Today, you are safe.

I ended up having another EFT session with Corby and we talked about my past relationships. This is where the forgiving me part comes in. Oh, what a long list it was of not choosing the right people that were best for my heart. I never felt worthy of myself, and I didn't make the best choices of people to be involved in my life. I had low self-esteem. Looking back, I felt weak and guilty that I didn't just leave and get out of the bad relationships. I would always stay far too long in hopes that they might change – with my help of course. Isn't that what we all believe? We both agreed that that wasn't the right story. Corby mentioned that I was doing what I had to do to survive and stay safe under those circumstances. I was a fighter, and I was brave. It was okay to forgive myself for all of it and we worked through this together. It was after this session that I could see what kind of people I wanted to be in my life. I didn't have to settle for being mistreated any longer. I am worthy of love, starting with loving myself for everything that I am.

We also ended up talking about my public speaking fears and how I had done public speaking before; however it still was a concern for me, and I had some fear around this still. She suggested that my fear of public speaking was nowhere comparable to the relationship that I had been in before. Corby asked me if public speaking was harder than being in that relationship I replied without hesitation, "*No.*" If I could survive that, I could survive anything, especially public speaking! My view on both topics has changed since that day.

Trust yourself, you ARE stronger than you realize.

Action Step:

Are there painful things that are on your mind that you're still carrying around with you? Reach out to someone who does EFT and see if they can help you release those emotions and move forward in a more positive light. Also, note that you were doing the best you could at the time, and be sure to FORGIVE yourself!

EFT and Loving Yourself
Corby Furrow

"Life is now... tap in!"

~ Corby Furrow

I am an ordinary person on an extraordinary adventure! I used to cringe when people would say I was such a "good" athlete, artist, singer, mother, etc. I hated it because I didn't believe that I was worthy. I didn't want to be seen or be vulnerable, and I didn't think I was loveable. I certainly didn't love who I thought I was! Holding these beliefs about myself showed up in my life as an over-pleaser, having to make people happy at all costs to myself. I married someone I didn't want to marry because I thought no one else would love me. I would not accept any compliment and rejected them all, but I would lead or take charge and then fade into the background if I got noticed. I thought no one would notice me and I could just blend in.

Even though I had a successful career and family and continued to move up the career ladder, it was a struggle. I believed I wasn't smart and didn't bring any value. Despite that, I got the education, got the promotions, and excelled on the outside. It all felt fake on the inside- like I would be found out, at any moment. Thankfully, I had people who saw through my armour and could see who I was and who I could be. They kept nudging me forward. Part of me wanted to go there and part of me was terrified that I would be found out to be a fake or an imposter. It felt like smoke and mirrors.

When I lost my job as a Director of HR after 25 years, my worst fears came true. It was found out that I was a fraud. It only took 25 years to prove it! Here I was, without a job, purpose, or identity. There could be no other reason- I wasn't good enough! This was a low point for me. After losing my job, I lost my confidence and was afraid I would never be hired again because the new employers would see how much of a fake I was. I was telling myself all kinds of stories and the stories kept growing in my mind!

Then in my despair, I went to an event in Toronto to see if I wanted to become a coach. As fate would have it, I met some people who had a six-month program on healing yourself. I had no idea what it was about, but I knew this is what I needed. I signed up on the spot with no questions asked. I live in Alberta and I think my husband thought I had lost it by this time, but he kept that to himself.

A month later, I flew back to Toronto to start this journey. Little did I know that my life was about to go through another big change. We started tapping on our faces and body. I wanted to leave because I thought, "What foolishness is this?" Then, something happened. I felt lighter- the thing I had been working on, which was a trigger in my life, no longer had importance. Wow! There is something to this Emotional Freedom Technique (EFT) or tapping. I spent the next six months uncovering this feeling of unworthiness, not belonging, and not being good enough. It was hard, emotional and yet, on the other side, there was peace, relief, and a sense of knowing I was good enough. I even fell in love with myself!

This put me on a trajectory I didn't even know was possible. I liked EFT so much and knew that, if I could love myself and see that I am smart, worthy, did have skills and, was good at things, others could also have that. So, for the past six years, I have been continuously doing my work, training, and honing my skills as a Conscious EFT Practitioner. Now, I am also an advanced practitioner and Master EFT Trainer. To round it off, I also became a Certified Executive Coach.

Every day, I get to wake up and make a difference in this world by doing my work and becoming the best loving human being that I can be. Secondly, I get to help others bring this healing and peace into their lives and the lives of their families and friends. Thirdly, I get to teach others to add this modality to their toolboxes and create a larger healing ripple effect in our communities, country, and beyond.

What is this wonderful tool you ask? Great question by the way. EFT is a form of energy psychology. This is a branch of psychology that addresses the body and the mind systems to address the relationship between thoughts, feelings, and behaviours. This is one of the most powerful tools we have available today to address emotional stress and its associated symptoms in the areas of health, wealth, relationships, and work.

Conscious EFT™ is a trauma-informed approach to working with the human nervous system. Change can only happen in the here and now, so I work with clients with what is showing up today. It is important to build up the client's resilience or window of tolerance so that they can manage the anxieties and stresses that show up for them today. Once they have enough capacity, then we can move into deeper issues clearing out stuck emotions, thoughts, beliefs, and behaviours that hold the client back.

Conscious EFT™ is a gentle technique that allows for post-traumatic growth. The client needs to move forward into the life they dream of and not live in the residue of past painful traumas and beliefs. Using EFT removes the associated negative emotions from the memory, thus freeing the individual from paralyzing fear, stress, anxiety, and other emotional traps.

What I love about this technique is that stress management and symptom management it is at everyone's fingertips. If you are feeling stressed, overwhelmed, anxious, etc., all you have to do is start tapping. When we tap, it sends signals to the amygdala in the brain and lets it know it's okay to calm down and that you are okay at this moment. Clients can immediately deal with these feelings. For deeper work, it's best to work with an EFT Practitioner as they can see what we may not want to see.

Over 85% of mental and physical dis-ease have an underlying stress component. So, it makes sense that, when we reduce the stress and inflammation, there is a greater chance that our mental and physical well-being will improve. Therefore, EFT is such a powerful tool in healing mentally, physically, emotionally, and spiritually.

What does this mean for you? Whatever is holding you back, mentally, physically, or emotionally, there is a gentle way to deal with it and create the direction of life that you haven't even dared to dream yet. You are supported, can heal your life, and create more joy.

When we can, I work with people in person, over Zoom, or via phone and it is effective in all forms. This work isn't easy, but it is worth it. You are worth it!

Action Step:

Have you heard of EFT before? Is it something that you would consider using to add/help your life? Write down your thoughts about this topic.

Soul Retrieval –
The Truth of Your Fragmented Self
Rae-ann Wood-Schatz

"A simple touch of kindness can heal a wound of the soul which no medicine can touch."

~ Debasish Mridha

I had a soul retrieval session with Rae-ann and what came up for me was very enlightening. It brought me back to the exact moment where, last summer, I had given up on myself. I had been struggling to make things work for my business in Edmonton and I wondered what exactly I was working towards. Where is the joy? I couldn't find it. I couldn't find happiness. All I felt was an extreme feeling of loneliness. It was a harsh and cruel moment for me. I had given up inside, felt alone, and was slipping into a depression. I remember that moment all too well and I have lovingly forgiven myself for it.

They do say that, at some point in your life before getting diagnosed, you may have given up. When you weren't feeling happy, hurtful words might have passed your thoughts. Today, I regret saying those words to myself and even thinking about them at the time. Words do matter and our body, mind, and soul are listening. Our mind wants to make us happy and so thinking negative words can set negative things in motion. I realize now that I was never truly alone. All I had to do was ask for support, which is not always an easy thing to do. It is one of the hardest things for us to do... ask for support. It doesn't mean we are weak, it means we don't have to do EVERYTHING on our own. There are so many people around that can and want to help us. Let them help.

During this Soul retrieval process, another thought came to my mind-. the moment in the hospital when the neurosurgeon gave me my prognosis. It was grim- terminal cancer, where my estimated lifetime was averaging about one year. No hope was given to me at that moment. All I could do was cry and tell myself that this can't be happening. Not to me! If you have ever experienced this moment, which I hope you haven't, know that there is always hope no matter what the situation is. **I REALLY can't stress this point enough. There's always more that can be done.** If I can heal my body, mind, and spirit, I know that you can, too. Read on to see what Rae-ann says about the topic.

What is the Soul?

It can be defined as the essence that gives rise to the consciousness of a living being. Souls are incorporeal, meaning that they transcend beyond the physical. It can also be described as a distinct entity that can exist without a body. The soul is your life energy, and your human body is contained within it. It gives awareness to your body, and provides you the ability to think, sense, analyze, feel emotions, and have memories. The soul expresses itself through a person's personality. Without knowing exactly what the soul is, and what your soul is like, you can easily get stuck, lost, or stranded. In essence, it is your "true" nature. As all of life at its core is energy, a soul could be imagined as the whole of this energy or the total that animates, moves, and speaks to us in the quiet moments when we are searching for guidance.

If we understand the soul as the unique essence or essential life force of something, we can then see that everything has a soul because everything has a one-of-a-kind life force energy. No two things in existence are the same, including identical twins, who do have some differences. For example, if you went outside in nature and paid attention to the trees around you, you may discover that each one has a certain uniqueness, not only in appearance, but also in energy. It is the energy that is the 'soul' of the tree. The same could be said for anything you come across- a dog, a bird, a cloud, a mountain, a lake, etc. Everything has a specific "such-ness" that differentiates it from other things. Even the world, Mother Earth, Gaia has a soul! The world's soul is often referred to or known as anima mundi or the universal soul because it encompasses all beings. It is essentially the total of all energy as well as the manifestation, and the essence of all beings.

The question has occasionally been asked if a person can be born without a soul. For example, do serial killers or psychopaths have a soul? In Shamanism, it is believed that we are all born with souls, and it's just some people's lost connection to them due to ancestral, society, familial, and childhood trauma. Sometimes, this trauma is so intense that the person loses complete connection with their soul. It is barricaded and 'missing' from the essence of the person and is why despicable acts of cruelty can be committed by someone who, in essence, no longer feels anything or becomes obsessed by rage.

Shamanic Teacher Christa Mackinnon says, *"it is our soul that provides us with a kind of inner voice, a moral compass, and direction. It is our soul that we hear as this 'little voice inside' reminding us that there is more we can become, and it is our soul that suffers when we don't nourish it by integrating a spiritual component into our lives and striving to give our lives meaning*

177

and purpose." So, imagine this as being someone who has become completely disassociated from their soul and has no moral compass or inner voice.

In essence, the soul connects you to your higher purpose and helps you lead a grounded, moral life. It guides you toward wholeness.

Many people think that the soul is a little twenty-one-gram "thing" that exists within the body- the movie "21 Grams" popularized this idea. Or, people are confused about the difference between the soul and spirit. Whereas the soul relates to the energy of the earth and human existence, the spirit relates to heaven. The soul is a doorway into the mysteries of the personal unknown, and the spirit opens a door into boundless oneness. The soul is experienced in the subconscious, or lower world, realms and spirit is encountered in states of super consciousness, or upper world levels. When we can tap into both states, we experience mystical feelings of bliss. Summarize it like this- your soul is earthly, mysterious, and accessed through the subconscious in dreams and visions. Spirit is more heavenly, content, free and accessed through states of purified awareness like meditation, plant medicine, and other forms of altering states.

In certain Shamanic traditions, it has been said that the soul is contained in the luminosity, or the energy field, that sits just outside the body. It is also believed that, when trauma occurs, it is not unusual to have a piece of the soul fragment from the energy field and disappear into the Spirit World, taking the trauma or the suffering along with it. It will then hold it "away" from the person until either the person dies, and the soul is reunited with all fragments, or until the person calls it back.

Why Soul Loss Occurs

Stressful situations are inevitable in life. A person may go through traumatic situations during their life, which can leave feelings of hopelessness and devastation. To help the body cope with the pain and prevent it from fully experiencing the impact of the trauma and ensure survival, a part of the soul leaves the body. It can happen at any time in your life, and it doesn't only happen when you experience physical trauma. It can also be caused by emotional and psychological trauma, but also during significant soul loss in an individual. Examples of events that can create soul loss are accidents, physical or emotional abuse, war, major surgery or illness, community violence, natural disasters, breakups or divorce, death, rejection, oppression, bullying, prolonged grief, or a humiliating experience. It can and does happen in childhood and adulthood. Because we have different viewpoints and different coping skills, what causes trauma in one person may not be the same for another. So, consider a traumatic experience as something that negatively affects the natural condition of the soul.

How Do We Experience Soul Retrieval?

Soul retrieval is a spiritual practice of reintegrating the soul fragments into the person's body. It is done to heal soul loss and recover one's true self. With the help of a soul retrieval technique, lost fragments can be called back either with the help of a spiritual guide or with your intent. In ancient times, soul retrieval healing would be done as soon as it was understood that there has been a soul loss. Today, many people spend large parts of their lives dealing with significant soul loss. You often feel lost or disconnected. You may unknowingly use phrases like 'I feel like something is "missing," "I'm not like I used to be," or "I don't know what to do now." You will have feelings of being incomplete, having a lack of confidence, a feeling of an inner void, feeling stuck, depression, memory loss, PTSD, chronic anxiety, self-deprecation, or even immunity issues.

In traditional times, the Shaman would be the one to journey to the Spirit World and bring back the fragmented parts and then, with drumming and breathwork, "re-insert" the separated parts back into the person's energy field. Hypnosis is a newer, very effective way for a person to call the parts back themselves. The therapist can simply guide the trance state and suggest the personal journey into an altered state of consciousness, whereby they can, without re-experiencing past trauma, heal the same said past experiences and call back the energy parts that leave a person feeling 'not complete', or feeling like a part of them is 'missing'. Subsequently, the person can then function from a more integrated place in their lives, feeling 'whole' and grounded. At the end of the day, the person undergoing soul retrieval must be completely willing and prepared for the positive change. Even after a session, the individual needs to actively work on healing their soul, especially if it's the first step in their healing journey.

What Can I Expect After?

Soul retrieval can bring about many positive changes. Benefits such as feeling a sense of fullness and safety, being more connected to your higher self, having greater clarity, gaining a new perspective, developing a greater ability to make decisions, feeling hopeful, and being better able to deal with negative emotions come along with a greater sense of purpose, increased ability to let go of bad experiences, better health and feeling more alive, and most importantly, a sense of joy.

After completion of the soul retrieval process, the client is also able to regain the skills, knowledge, strengths, and abilities that were taken by the soul fragment during soul loss.

Suffice it to say, there is virtually nothing to lose by deciding to incorporate soul work into your growth and healing journey and, if you feel the call, I am happy to be your guide.

Action Step:

How do you feel about Soul Retrieval? Write down your thoughts about this topic and choose whether it is something that is needed in your life.

Spiritual Response Therapy
Elise Brathwaite

"When everything seems uncertain, anything becomes possible."

~ Unknown

When I was first asked to take part in this amazing book, it was an immediate YES! I could see and appreciate the huge opportunity that having this significant piece to the healing journey puzzle included would mean for anyone reading this down the road. What I didn't consider is how hard it would be to explain the Universe, portals, dimensions, past lives, akashic records, energy, soul-self versus the human-self, and magic overall, in words. And so, my invitation to you is to lean into the experience of this next chapter as it will be a healing experience all of its own.

Allow your mind to consider potentials you may have never been open to before. Even if just for this moment, as you read each of these words, you allow yourself to let go of everything you thought you knew and be open to remembering a pearl of deep and ancient wisdom that lies deep within you.

You will also want to hang on to these acronyms I have created as they will be used throughout this chapter!

YCMTSU - You Can't Make This Shit Up!

MDOG – Modern Day Oracle Goddess
IFLY – I Fucking Love You
RTA – Real Time Ascension
WPS – Well Played Spirit

My name is Elise, and I am the proud mum of two amazing sons and two fur babies. I come from a loving, fiery Irish mum, and a feisty, ridiculous Barbadian father. Let's just say life as a biracial child born in the early '80s in small-town Edmonton, Alberta, to an unwed 17-year-old Irish Catholic mother and a transient highly ADHD father proved to be interesting. Every ounce of my early experiences shaped, molded, and stretched me into becoming who I am today.

Today, I proudly affirm I am a Modern Day Oracle Goddess (MDOG), Soul Speaker & Sage, and a Spiritual Response Therapy Consult. As an MDOG, I act as a bridge between the physical world and the Spirit world. I can be a clear channel for Spirit to deliver messages to you. This allows me to converse effectively with your High Self and, by relaying these messages back to you, it always feels like a message delivered directly from home. As a modern Sage, I am keenly attuned to my inner voice, the wisdom that sits deep within my womb. I am on an internal soul journey in search of deep remembrance of who I AM, and what brings meaning to my existence, meaning to the struggles and suffering of the human experience in the systematic chaos, or what we call the world.

Now, let me tell you about how I manifest all these gifts because there is no sense in having them if I am not going to put them to good use, right? So, this is where it gets interesting.

Spiritual Response Therapy (SRT) was developed by former Unity minister, Robert E. Detzler in 1988. SRT is a direct and precise healing technique that works on a spiritual level to eliminate spiritual, mental, emotional, and physical blocks and challenges. It is a process of bypassing the conscious mind to research the subconscious mind and soul records to find and release the discordant and limiting energies and beliefs that are blocking and limiting your life. The research is accomplished with the use of muscle response, a pendulum as a movement amplifier, a set of channeled charts, and tapping into higher guidance. The alchemy of these tools helps in identifying past life energies, subconscious blocks, and negative soul programming that is ready to be cleared from the subconscious and soul's akashic records. The result of this work enables you to live a happier, healthier, more purposeful, and joy-filled life. These sessions provide clarity for your current situation through the understanding of your soul records, thereby allowing you to harmonize your relationships and to feel more empowered to create the life you desire. Remembering that, by changing your inner landscape, you will start to reflect and experience the healthier, happier version of you in your outer world.

So that was fun, right? Makes perfect sense? No, seriously, what does this all mean? To break it down, let me give you a couple of analogies to help bring some clarity. We know that energy is not created or destroyed, it is only transformed. Now, although this might push against some beliefs for you, you've already agreed that you're willing to be open, so take a deep breath as I venture into this next piece. Have you ever wondered why you have an affinity for certain cultures, foods, music? Have you ever just yearned to travel to a different part of the world, and you can't explain that pull? Have you ever dreamt that you were in Egypt, or Atlantis, or perhaps fighting a saber tooth tiger? Have you ever had an odd affinity for a certain era in time or dove deeply into every detail about something that seems to have no meaning to anyone else? What if I were to tell you that this is part of the now you, remembering a part of the old you?

What do I mean about the old you? I'm so happy you asked! Let me put it to you this way- we are souls, an emanation of pure Divine consciousness. We reincarnate multiple times throughout our soul's evolution for learning, growing, descending, and expanding consciousness. Because we have incarnated many times, over many eras, over many dimensions, and even in many Universes, we accumulate both positive and negative energies as a direct result of these lifetimes. These energies get stored in a sort of Soul Bank, or a type of Records, known as your Akashic Records. These akashic records store all of the lifetimes that you have ever experienced.

Let me explain a little how this works on my end. One of my gifts is clairvoyance, meaning that I can see the unseen. How the akashic records look to me is like a big Vault, holding thousands and thousands of books and pamphlets, and paper stapled together depending on the length, importance, severity of any lifetime.

Why do we incarnate? I'll break it down quickly here for you, too. Imagine that each lifetime you incarnate is like coming to school- some of the things you will come in to learn are part of the curriculum and some of the others are electives. I know sometimes we struggle through our core subjects, and we need to get tutors, or study groups together and sometimes we need to outright retake that class. Now, in this Vault of your akashic records, you have an entire section in this Library titled "me in romantic relationships," or "me in leadership," or "me and money!" Now, at any given time, these sections of your Library might have giant encyclopedias, small pamphlets, and everything in between. The purpose of using SRT is to dive as far back as we need to go to access the most prominent lifetime in which energy is being stored at the root, but it's being played out energetically in the now. Often when I'm working with clients about their past lives, I will hear them

186

say: *"Are you sure you're not talking about right now, this is my life today!"*

You see, we are living in an illusion-type state until we wake up. If you think of your life and every situation, event, and interaction like scenes from a movie, then you will also recognize every person who comes into the scene as another character supporting you in your lead role!

It is said that you will only find SRT when you are truly ready for that level of healing and, while that time came full circle for me in 2014, it all started for me with my spiritual awakening in 2006. That started with a good old-fashioned near-death experience. I didn't know it at the time, but this set the course for a full transformation of my life and the lives of those around me. Since that experience, my life has been full of magic, YCMTSU moments, RTAs, and a multitude of opportunities for me to level up and further remember who I AM.

In 2010, I was in an extremely toxic relationship with someone who exhibited high narcissistic tendencies. I had two little boys that I was caring for full-time as a single parent, and I was a proud owner of a booming nail business. Through a series of synchronicities, a new nail client enters my scene, and equipped with the perfect script Crystal, notices that my hands are heating up as I am working on her nails and she asks, *"Do you practice Reiki?"* I had not heard of Reiki before that moment, but my womb was yelling yes, and I wanted to know more. I started studying with her and completed my Usui Reiki Holy Fire Master Teacher under her mentorship.

Everything about Reiki practice felt right! This is what I was unconsciously doing already with nail clients- healing, guiding, clearing, and releasing. It's why they would leave feeling so clear and empowered and why I would leave feeling so drained. By taking Reiki training, I was able to harness my energy and stop giving from my stores of energy and learn to access the energy that's available all around us.

187

This brought more balance, support, and direction into my life and, as a result, I expanded my business to include Reiki sessions, which had become very popular. As my Reiki practice began to grow, I felt more alive and on purpose than I ever had before! I had a repeat clientele and, based on past business strategy, the addition of my Reiki practice felt expansive and like a good business system.

One day, my regular client, Josh, who had a lot of life stresses happening simultaneously, came in for his monthly session. We had been working together for months by then, and I was noticing a theme with him. He would come in for his session and I would get to work with all hands and forces of light on deck. I could feel the heavy and thick energy and I would often see it as dark smoke or sometimes sludgy liquid circling in his energy centres. After an hour or so of work, his energy field would begin to glow with clear white light or sometimes gold like sun rays. He would feel light and at ease and, a month later, we would start all over again. I was beginning to wonder if there was something else I needed to add to my sessions or something else I needed to learn that would enhance my Reiki sessions, leaving a more permanent effect or something that would get to the root of the problem.

If you have ever been interested in taking a spiritual development course, then you know how many amazing and exciting things there are to learn out there. My Aquarian energy coupled with ADD had me buzzing with ideas, which lead me to all the things and ultimately to nothing! So, I decided to get quiet, go within, and have a very clear ask from Spirit and it sounded something like this "*Spirit, guide me to whatever it is that is next for me, whatever it is that will support me in providing healing that will be lasting, even permanent, whatever it is that will get these blocks and energies from the root of the problem. Oh! And one more thing Spirit, make the message loud! So loud I can't miss it, it needs to either land in my lap or slap me in the face.*"

Now, to be very clear, I respect Reiki as a healing modality, and I go for sessions with a very gifted practitioner. This adjustment in my Reiki practice was simply Spirit directing me to the next level of my purpose: SRT.

Fast forward to January 2014, after a roller coaster ride of a backstory and another series of synchronicities, I find myself in the beautiful Rocky Mountains of Jasper Alberta, doing nails at a local salon to help a business owner who had torn her rotator cuff. On this day, I found myself meeting the most magical human being with whom I had an immediate soul recognition. You know, that feeling when you just remember somebody or when you feel like you've known them your whole life-, that was my experience of meeting Margo, a complete soul connection, reunited with a long-lost sister. Shortly after meeting this magical queen, I ended my time in Jasper but our journey together was only beginning.

In August of 2014, Margo came to my city, and we met up for dinner. It was already feeling like an auspicious meeting because the stars had aligned for me to be available the one day that she was available to meet up. We got in with a last-minute reservation to the restaurant we had wanted. As we are being guided to our table, I see that we are headed in the direction of a giant booth that is typically assigned to large parties. We both chuckled at this and started to slide our butts around the large booth until we were both sitting on the long side of the table, legs crossed on the bench facing each other as though we were curled up on a couch about to share makeup tips. We got as far as ordering a beverage when Margo turns to me, stares me dead in the soul, SLAPS ME ON MY LAP, and says "*Oh my God, there's a course you need to take!*" At that moment, I felt my soul snap backward out of my body, all the sound left my ears, and it was as though time stood in the quantum field. As quickly as this experience took, the coming back happened as quickly. Time sped up like I was fast-forwarding a VHS, muffled sounds started to flood back into my ears until there was almost a sharp ringing, and I felt my soul snap back in. Then I heard, *"Elise, listen."* I don't know how long that moment lasted in this reality, but it felt like I had hovered outside of my body for at least five minutes before I came back fully. There was the sign I had been waiting for as I had asked Spirit to make the message loud and obvious! I had requested that it land in my lap or slap me in the face! Well, I got both and a slap in the lap! It's important to be open to interpreting the magic of messages from Spirit. WPS!

This magical queen who is equally floating in the clouds like me tells me one thing and one thing only about this course. She says to me, *"You have to take this class! It's like Cosmic Reiki clearing."* So, equipped with that one statement, the experience of my soul snapping out of my body and the synchronicity of her slapping my leg, I said, "Sign me up," and the rest has been a magical rainbow ride through the quantum field of dimensions and realities. My gifts have strengthened. My clairvoyant, telepathic, and psychic abilities have increased ten-fold and, as I write this today, I have released a toxic relationship, and now have a wonderful partner. I have fully released my nail business and joyfully moved into this calling and purpose with ease, abundance, and support from the Universe. I have invited new authentic friendships and support systems into my life, taken multiple additional spiritual training to add to my tool kit, and am working on my teaching certification as this medicine needs to have further reach in the world.

I could go on for days telling you about clearings I have had or done on myself. I could tell you all the amazing minutia of how I finally released myself from a toxic relationship as well as the habits and beliefs that drew that curriculum into my life in the first place. I could share about the time I was clearing in a courthouse and set off all the alarms in the entire building and the whole place had to be evacuated! I could share all the miracles I've witnessed through SRT, all the YCMTSU moments, and RTAs, but the truth is every session, with every person, is a unique miracle. Over the years, I have provided thousands of clearings and have had the privilege of witnessing the benefits of SRT and support many people who were blocked and struggling to figure out why they couldn't get pregnant, find the relationship they so desired, or why they struggled with their health, body, mental health, money, self-worth, addictions, and self-love. The challenge someone is experiencing that will finally lead them to me will vary, but what is ultimately the same in each person is that they are at their wit's end, have done and tried everything they can think of, taken the courses, gotten the therapist or the life coaches, and read the books, so they are finally open to something else that will help them see what they cannot and will end their suffering.

I have had people come in for infertility and then had pictures of the positive pregnancy test, ultrasounds, and newborn babies sent to me! I have cleared my mum of past lives in the Irish famine and of her fear of having her home taken away, which was blocking her from feeling worthy of even applying for a mortgage. She has now owned her home for three years! I have supported people in relationships that were about to end for unexplainable reasons but are now happily still together. I have cleared people of soul contracts with old lovers that they were not able to let go of and let new love into their lives. In the case of my beautiful soul sister, Tanya, I went into higher realms when she was undergoing surgery. I saw her meeting her mom, feeling her love, and not being sure if she wanted to come back. I saw her mom holding her and I saw her choose to come back and fight! This woman is a warrior, let me tell you!

I worked on her brain and on the doctors and nurses that were supporting her to ensure they were all clear and able to help her through this. During her recovery, we worked

191

together and sometimes I worked on her alone because I got the "hit" from Spirit that she needed extra support that day. I cleared her blood, lymphatic systems, etheric body, past lives, and other relationships in her life. Whatever Spirit threw our way, we cleared it! And while SRT was only one part of her commitment to living, she has shared with me how deeply our clearings have transformed her life. I love this woman, my soul sister, infinitely and I am so proud of her for taking this experience and sharing it with the world so she can inspire and empower others who may be feeling like there's no hope. IFLY Tanya, in this lifetime and beyond!

My mission in life is to educate, awaken, and inspire myself and others to clear their limiting beliefs and spiritual blocks so they can experience a deeper relationship with who they are and have that love of self and inner knowing of ultimate worthiness be reflected in their everyday life. I am here to help you remember.

I hope you have enjoyed this chapter and all the juicy wisdom in this book. I would like to leave you with one last thought, quite possibly the most important one for us all to remember.

"Our deepest fear is not that we are inadequate. Our deepest fear is that we are powerful beyond measure. It is our light, not our darkness that most frightens us. We ask ourselves, 'Who am I to be brilliant, gorgeous, talented, fabulous?' Actually, who are you not to be? You are a child of God. Your playing small does not serve the world. There is nothing enlightened about shrinking so that other people won't feel insecure around you. We are all meant to shine, as children do. We were born to make manifest the glory of God that is within us. It's not just in some of us; it's in everyone. And as we let our own light shine, we unconsciously give other people permission to do the same. As we are liberated from our own fear, our presence automatically liberates others."

~ Marianne Williamson

Principle of Healing IV

Discover Your Destiny by Raising Your Vibrations

Time to Up-Level Your Life in a Big Incredible Way

Electro Magnetic Fields and Frequencies (EMF's)

"Be the energy you want to attract."

~ Unknown

While healing my body, I was looking for a way to help bring in some income and also help others. I said to the Universe, higher power, whatever you would refer to "it" as that I am open to new opportunities that present themselves to me. So, when an Electromagnetic Field (EMF) pendant was gifted to me, I looked it up online, saw an opportunity, and said, "YES!" I started sharing EMF pendants and EMF brainwave protectors on my social media. EMFs are the frequencies that are emitted from any wireless device- laptops, cell phones, Bluetooth, wireless keyboards, video game controllers, etc. Having a pendant on, or putting a brainwave protector on your device, can protect you from harmful radiation. We emit our frequency around us whether it be a positive vibration such as love, or gratitude or a negative one such as anger or hate. The opposite is true of wireless devices. They send out a frequency as well, only this one can be harmful to our bodies. This is my opinion, do your research, but please don't ever put a cell phone next to your ear. At the very least, use a pair of earbuds or a speaker phone. Scientifically, not doing so may harm your brain over time.

I also made sure not to have any Wi-Fi in my bedroom as well, not even my cell phone. An extra tip from my friend Karen was to use a Christmas tree timer to turn off my Wi-Fi at night so there was nothing on while I slept. There was no need to turn it on or off daily, which is brilliant really. Set it and forget it!

I am creating My New Reality, one day at a time, by tapping into my higher energetic frequency, putting thoughts out, and seeing the results come back to me.

Here were my predictions for my future as I create them:

- In 2021, my cancer will be gone and never return
- I will have a best-selling book on Amazon
- I will be an inspirational speaker in demand for positivity and doing the 'impossible'
- I will meet Joe Dispenza in person
- I will be living somewhere with no snow with my kind loving husband
- I will have a personal chef and trainer
- I will never worry about finances again

If you want to raise your frequency, add more love and thoughts of gratitude into your day, as these are the highest vibrational frequencies. Did you know that expressing gratitude for ten minutes a day increases your immune system and the effects linger most of the day? Imagine if you did 3 to 10 minutes a day of gratitude, how would that affect your life and affect your future? On the other hand, if you spend ten minutes obsessing over something that is hurtful and sit in that negative thought, you can reduce your immune system and open the door to dis-ease. Let's take some time and be grateful even if it's being grateful for things that have not happened yet in life. We can visualize them instead and make them happen simply by thinking about some of them every day. We can create our future and be thankful because we can make it anything we want it to be!

Action Step:

Make a list of how many WI-FI devices are in your home. This could be cell phones, cordless home phones, microwaves, televisions especially HD sets, refrigerators, hairdryers, computers, monitors, laptops, video game systems, Bluetooth, or any other wireless devices. What can you do to reduce your exposure to these frequencies?

Meditations, Mantras, and Yoga
Danielle Beaulieu

"She believed she could, so she did."

~ R.S. Grey

My friend Danielle recently started a yoga and meditation practice and we've been regularly doing mantras and meditation on Sunday afternoons. When I first was diagnosed with Glioblastoma, I spent a couple of weeks in the hospital after my surgery. Danielle had recently lost her dog and I knew it was going to be a rough time for her. I felt a little guilty being in the hospital because I was worried about her. I didn't want another bad thing to happen. I was so excited when she told me she had gotten this opportunity to go to Greece and study yoga, meditation, and mantras. She was going away while I was in the hospital, and I knew it would be life-changing for her and, little did I know, that it was also going to be life-changing for me as well.

I have been enjoying meditations with Dee, specifically a healing Kundalini mantra, Ra ma da sa. Thank you so much, Dee, for sending me a video of everyone in your class doing this Kundalini mantra. It was so powerful and touched my heart deeply. We started out practicing this mantra together every Sunday with a small group of people. It was relaxing and very therapeutic. Another one is "I am Bliss," which I play every morning to set my intention for the day. It always makes me feel good and, if I start singing in my head, at least I'm singing a good tune. I'm still learning about different meditations. Some nights, I put on my Galaxy Cove in my bedroom, watching the colourful lights circle past me while listening to this relaxing meditation. It kind of reminds me of the Aurora Borealis, which hopefully I have seen by now. It looks so magical!

Here is what Danielle wanted to share.

Yoga

During a routine checkup, my family doctor suggested I try Yoga. I laughed! Me? Yoga? No thanks! For someone who was in MMA training six days a week while playing and coaching ice hockey, Yoga was too slow for this gal! But, at every appointment, she would tell me the same thing, "*You need to do Yoga.*"

So finally, I tried it and HATED IT! It was everything I thought it would be, except it was HARD! It was hard because it was slow. It was mindful. And I was in my head too much.

For some reason, though, I found myself attending a class here and there. I would go with a friend or go if a friend of mine was teaching a class. I remember my first few classes, standing in Warrior II pose, thinking about was how much my arms and legs were hurting! I thought I was fit! We would then move on to a "recovery pose" of Downward Facing Dog and, for the life of me, I couldn't figure out how this pose was meant to be restful.

I was by no means a yogi, but I put up with the practice now and then. I figured that, to hate it this much, I must be doing it wrong when everyone else was loving it right? I had to figure this out. I am not a quitter, so I tried different styles of Yoga and my practice slowly evolved over the years and became more consistent and regular. I was finally getting it!

Yoga is called a practice because it's something you are constantly working on. There is no end goal or perfection. It's not about being better than the person next to you. Instead, it's about being better than you were yesterday. Yoga is a 'competition' with yourself only and your ego! It's not about being able to touch your toes, but what you learn on the way down. It's not about toning your butt but getting your head out of it.

The lineage of Yoga dates back more than 3000 years, and the word 'Yoga' means 'to yoke' or 'bring together'. Therefore, Yoga is the merging or uniting of opposites. It is about finding balance and bringing together differences. This could be interpreted as the balance of mind and body and many aspects within all of us i.e., active/receptive, cool/hot, sun/moon, joy/sadness, contraction/expansion, male/female energy, etc.

If you're only doing the physical Asanas, or poses of Yoga, you're not truly doing Yoga, but exercise. Since it has the same benefits as regular exercise, this is still great! Of course! But what makes Yoga different from any other type of exercise is what is called the "8 Limbs of Yoga." They are laid out in Patanjali's Yoga Sutra and are like a road map on the spiritual journey. They are a list of instructions, moral guidelines, or practices and disciplines to help reach a more connected, spiritual state– that is what we're all aiming for.

I'm not here to teach religion, nor am I a believer in religion, but I am a believer in Spirituality. I grew up in a Christian home with Christian beliefs and the name "God", but throughout this chapter, I will interchangeably refer to "Universe", "Spirit", "Self" or "Intuition" as well. I am still struggling with what to call 'It' without being disrespectful to the incredibly powerful 'Being' I KNOW exists. I do not see Yoga as a religion, and I am in no way encouraging you to change your religion or belief system. Many of the "rules" of religion cross over from one to the other in one form or another and you find the same within Yoga as well. We can all agree that there are certain standards to not living life as a complete idiot.

Each limb relates to a specific way of interacting with the world through ethics and consciousness to achieve a healthy and fulfilling life. The first six limbs are actions to take, and the last two limbs are what happens because of the practice.

The Eight Limbs of Yoga are:

1. Yamas

Like "The Ten Commandments," they are a code of Ethical Principles for living soulfully. The Yamas are not just about how we interact with others, but also how we interact with ourselves every day. The Yamas consist of the following principles:

Ahimsa = Compassion for all living things

This extends beyond physical harm and includes verbal, sexual, and emotional harm. Ahimsa asks us to look at the language we use and ensure that we are acting in a way that is non-harmful to ourselves and others.

Satya = Truthfulness

Practicing Satya means adhering to a truthful way of living in our interactions with ourselves and others. Satya means committing to being honest with others, refraining from gossip, and living in a way that is true to who we are as individuals. Before you speak T.H.I.N.K. = Is it True, Helpful, Interesting, Necessary, Kind?

Asteya = Non-Stealing

Asteya means not taking anything that isn't freely given. Nothing is truly yours that you can't take with you. This also means being mindful of others' time.

Bramacharya = Mindful Conservation of Energy

Often translated as celibacy, this Yama is concerned with using our energy consciously and wisely. I know today, celibacy isn't common practice, but because sexual energy is so powerful, it's about being mindful and okay with your sexual decisions.

Aparigraha = Non-Hoarding

This Yama is about controlling excess. Take what you need and nothing more. Don't let things define you and understand the difference between having and being attached to something. This extends beyond "stuff" and includes our behaviours in relationships and what we take from the earth in general.

Do you see the correlation to these principles across different religions? You may help it settle better by comparing these ideas to how your religious practice defines these principles. Asteya is like "Thou shall not steal" as expressed in the Ten Commandments as followed by Catholics, Christians, and the Jewish Torah.

2. Niyamas

Where the Yamas are like "The Ten Commandments", the Niyamas are a set of Disciplines and Practices, or "Commandments for Self" to observe in your life when dealing with yourself and others.

Shaucha = Cleanliness / Purity

This is practiced by maintaining cleanliness in body, mind, and surroundings. "Cluttered Mind = Cluttered Space, Cluttered Space = Cluttered Mind." Think about how it feels to walk into a cluttered room, full of unfinished projects, scattered dishes, and dust bunnies. Then think of how it feels to sniff the fresh laundry smell that lingers after all the clean laundry has been put away, or you finish tidying up the kitchen after cooking. It's about making choices about what you want and don't want in your life. That extends to objects, environments, and people. The practice of Shaucha allows us to live life more vividly.

Ways to practice Shaucha are chanting, using meditation to cleanse the mind, burning sage, or using of crystals to cleanse the space along with incorporating Yoga, Ayurveda, and clean eating to cleanse the body.

Santosha = Contentment

This is about being happy with where you are and what you have, not what your expectations are. Contentment is not about being happy, and it also doesn't mean we accept or tolerate unhealthy relationships or conditions. It simply means that we have to be okay with what is, and not compare things to how we expect them to be.

Meditations in which you free your mind of expectations, or Gratitude Journaling, in which you list five things that you are grateful for every day, are some ideas to practice Santosha. The more specific, the better. Instead of simply writing, "I am grateful for my friend, Tanya", I would say "I am grateful that Tanya called to check on me because she knew I had an appointment today."

Tapas = Burning Enthusiasm

This is not only for your belly! Tapas translates to "fire" or "heat", and it is the disciplined use of our energy. This comes from directing all your energy into something. That passion you feel for a project, what motivates you out of bed in the morning– that's your Tapas! It's about creating and defining your priorities.

Physical workouts that encourage sweating, like hot Yoga or cardio, address physical Tapas. Self-discipline, writing lists, or being accountable to friends which creates motivation are other examples of Tapas.

Svadhyaya = Self-Study

Regardless of whether you do it through art, writing, physical activity, or meditation, Svadhyaya is any opportunity that allows you to know yourself better. It helps us to understand our motives, thoughts, and desires more clearly. It's about seeing your life as sacred and therefore, in turn, treating your actions more objectively. The focus is on moving forward instead of judging yourself every day for past choices or behaviours and being more compassionate towards yourself. It is a big task to see yourself as you truly are. Go easy on yourself.

Isvara Pranidhana = Surrendering to Spirit

In this practice, we recognize that there is an omnipresent force larger than ourselves that is guiding and directing the course of our lives. We recognize that the things that happened in our life that were necessary for our growth. It's about listening to your intuition and trusting your gut. Give in to your ideas, but don't become complacent either. It's being an active participant in your life while trusting the process.

3. Asana – Postures – What people interpret as 'Yoga'

This is the most recognized limb and how people traditionally tend to get into the practice of Yoga. If you're only doing this part though, you're doing only exercise, not Yoga.

The word 'Asana' usually is translated as "pose" or "posture" but it means "comfortable seat." These physical postures were created to specifically help yogis sit comfortably in meditation for long periods. Our worlds are so busy! We are always doing multiple things at once. We are eating while watching tv, on the phone while driving, and cooking dinner while chatting to a loved one about their day. We're constantly split, and while we think we are great multi-taskers, we are also doing a great job of disassociating our bodies and minds. We are not mindfully eating and therefore often overeating. We become so split that we lose who we are. We're "doing" something to the body, instead of getting inside of it and becoming it. Yoga is the mind-body marriage and the Asanas help us with the physical part of that connection. Opening the physical body also helps create space for a more profound connection to the energetic body. The practice of Yoga will change how you interact with both your inner and outer worlds and the Asanas create a healthy and stable physical body to support a deeper spiritual journey. These poses are not only physical, but also have a psychological effect because many poses demand that you use your body in a different way, which can be challenging! In these moments, we need to be able to breathe and be comfortable with being uncomfortable. Certain Asanas or Yoga practices can benefit through realignment or focus on chakras too!

4. Pranayama – Breathwork

Pranayama works closely with the Asanas, focusing on and directing the breath, which can either create heat and energy or soothe and calm you. There are many different breathwork techniques such as what I would call "4x4". You inhale for four counts, hold for four counts, exhale for four counts and hold for four counts. Repeat the cycle four times. You could also inhale for four counts, hold for four counts and exhale for eight counts. When you control your breathing and your exhale is longer than your inhale, you are triggering the nervous system to relax. Other breathing techniques include 'Viloma Pranayama', 'Kumbhaka', 'Ujai Breath', and 'Nadi Shodhana'. Breathwork does have contraindications for some and can be a trigger with physical conditions such as anxiety, high blood pressure, pregnancy, heart disease, and some others, so please seek guidance before trying it, especially with heating breaths.

Heating breaths such as the Breath of Fire are cleansing and purifying and are more intense.

5. Pratyahara – Withdrawal of Senses

Practices such as meditation are Pratyahara, a practice of non-attachment to outside stimulus and a continuous focus to bring our mind and thoughts back to the present moment. This allows us to draw less and less on outward stimuli, and instead, draws our attention to our inner energy and intuition. It's funny how the withdrawal of senses can make your senses stronger.

A few years ago, I committed to learning meditation. I wanted to reap all the benefits I was hearing about it because Gawd knows I could use it! So, I prepared my space, prepared myself, was all proud, sat, closed my eyes, and took a deep breath... alright, we're doing this. I couldn't last two minutes! My active monkey brain danced about in my head. Come on! Sit down! I grew so frustrated with the monkey mind and myself that I got up and carried on with the list of things I apparently MUST do NOW.

Meditation is NOT easy, but it IS worth it! Get used to setting the commitment of time and the focus will come. Pratyahara is the start of meditation towards the path of Dhyana and there is more than one way to get there. Meditation takes many shapes. During my Yoga training, I became friends with one of the other students who happened to already be a Kundalini Yoga Teacher. She shared with me the deep impact of how Kundalini changed her life and introduced me to the practice. I am not a trained Kundalini Yoga Teacher; however, I have adapted to the Kundalini Mantra Meditations and have found them to be very beneficial for someone with an active mind like mine.

This mantra translates to "mind-tool", and these are words or phrases that are repeated over and over. Sometimes, it's a word that is repeated on inhaling and another on the exhale. This gives the mind something specific to focus on, which allows for deeper states of awareness. Mantras are very powerful because, the more you chant, the more you internalize the phrases or meanings. Yogis believe that, even if you don't understand the Sanskrit words of the mantra, they can still have a powerful effect due to the healing vibrations that resonate with each of the syllables recited. Remember how it was mentioned earlier in this book that your body listens? Some mantras are a specific "prayer", while others are just sound vibrations like "Om", which helps you connect to that frequency. While in my Yoga training and learning these techniques, it was at this time, that I, Tanya, and a group of friends began gathering regularly to do a Kundalini Healing Meditation "Ra Ma Da Sa".

6. Dharana – Intense Focus

As I sit writing this chapter, I am practicing Dharana. I am "in the zone." We've all experienced it. You know what I'm talking about, and it's a great feeling. Time flies, and you are taking names and rocking it! You have removed yourself from external distractions and your focus is laser sharp. The object of the focus is not important, it's the act of the focus itself that is Dharana.

Tanya began doing the "Ra Ma Da Sa" practice daily, and a group of us would gather weekly to do a "Care Bear Stare". Remember those? Meditation on its own is powerful, but meditating with a group of people who are sharing the same intention is SuperCharged! This intense Dharana was all supercharged energy towards Tanya and her healing. We saw healing water cascading from the Heavens, washing over and into her skull, cleansing away any signs of cancer and disease. We saw healthy brain cells growing and her physical body being filled with cleansing white light and guess what– it worked! We manifested our new realities.

There are many mantras within Kundalini Yoga and other practices, and they are not only specific to healing. There are some for opening specific Chakras, or for other health conditions. You can follow The Rock Yogi for my schedule of online group meditation sessions and some of my favourite meditation mantras.

If Mantras aren't your thing, there are other types of meditations, such as Breath Meditation, which involves focusing on your breath. Every time your mind gets distracted, you redirect it to the breath. This is what people traditionally interpret as 'Meditation' and. in my opinion, it is the most difficult. Japa Meditation involves meditating with a Mala to count the breath or recite a mantra, like a Catholic rosary. Candle gazing or object meditations are other forms. Personal favourites of mine include walking or moving meditations. Going for a hike in nature can also produce this. Any time you stop and mindfully pay attention to your experience and what is going on and are truly connected to the world around you, you are doing a form of mindfulness and meditation.

Points seven and eight are what happens when you practice points one through six.

7. **Dhyana** – State of Meditation

Dhyana is deeper than Pratyahara and is the sense of deep, profound, meditation. Your "Ah-Ha!" moment is when you tap in and feel connected to your intuition. Meditation allows your mind to rest and heal and it is here that we are open and can receive messages from Spirit and receive greater clarity.

Yogic science says that there are specific lengths of time needed for certain desired effects in meditation.

The benefits of meditation are well documented. Immediate results include a slower heart rate, release of physical tension, calmer mood and mindset. Long term effects of a continued regular practice includes greater relief of physical and stress-related pain, improved creativity, lower blood pressure, better decision making, greater resilience to stress, improved memory, intuition and ability to focus and concentrate, increased personal self-awareness, and improved emotional and mental stability. This creates new neural pathways between the left and right hemispheres of the brain, reducing cortisol levels. Do you need any more reasons? If so, ask Google – there are many more.

The length of your meditation practice matters, but you will feel results with even just a few minutes a day.

Three minutes affects blood circulation and electromagnetic field.

Eleven minutes changes glandular system and nerves.

Twenty-two minutes balances and coordinates the three minds.

Thirty-one minutes affects all the cells and rhythms of the body and all layers of the mind's projection.

Sixty-two minutes changes the gray matter of the brain and integrates the subconscious "shadow mind" and the outer projection.

Two and a half hours hold the new pattern in the subconscious mind by the surrounding universal mind.

Don't put any pressure on yourself to go from zero to sixty minutes. Remember, meditation is a practice that takes time and work. Begin with a commitment of three minutes a day. Even that can be tough when you start. Try different styles of meditation and see what resonates with you. With Kundalini meditation, you're meant to commit to a mantra that is recited daily for forty days. This is also called Sadhana, which means daily spiritual practice. It can be a mantra, ritual, prayer, journaling; whatever you choose that is a physical mindful act you perform. If you miss a day, you have to start back on day one. Forty days is represented throughout many religious texts as having significant meaning. Our bodies are constantly forming new cells and science has since discovered that, after forty days, you are essentially "newer" you than the old. So, the idea is that, by practicing Sadhana for forty continuous days, you will have incorporated that practice into the foundation of the new YOU. This helped me MAKE time in my day to do my meditation because I hated the idea of having to start all over! This worked for me, but whatever style you choose, remember to be comfortable and mindful of maintaining a straight spine. That way, the energy is free to move up and down through the central axis of the body. As the layers peel away, it is normal to be emotional during and after some meditations, even days later. Remember to be kind to yourself and view it as release and healing.

Samadhi – State of Oneness or Heavenly Bliss

This is the Ultimate Goal– Union with 'Self'. Everyone speaks of it as "Bliss", "Zen" or "Nirvana"– the feeling when you know we're all connected and made of the same.

Yoga didn't make its way to the Western world until 1893 where Swami Vivekenanda, the first Indian Monk to ever visit the West, demonstrated some Yoga postures at the Chicago World's Fair. His incredible physical feats, along with the Hindu texts he translated, fascinated the crowds and left a mark on Yoga in the West. Today, many styles of Yoga have emerged from these original teachings.

Depending on your needs or wants, there are many modern styles of Yoga:

Ashtanga Yoga

This is one of the two styles of Yoga in the world. There are six series, each with set postures to follow and each series getting progressively more challenging. A student may only move on to the next series after permission from a teacher. Only a few people have ever reached Level Five.

Bikram Yoga

Invented in 1977, it is the first form of hot Yoga, started by Bikram Choudy. It is a set series of 26 postures practiced in a room heated to 115 degrees Fahrenheit, or 45 degrees Celsius so that participants sweat to eliminate toxins.

Kundalini Yoga

Brought to the U.S. in the late 1960s, Kundalini is known as 'Yoga of awareness'. It focuses on awakening the spiritual energy through meditation, breathwork, and chanting.

Power Yoga

Often hot Ashtanga-inspired, this practice is a fast-paced vinyasa flow that gets your sweat on by focusing on breath, core, concentration, heat, and flow.

Yin Yoga

Popularized by Paul Grilley, this is a passive, stretching style practice is one where poses are held for three to five minutes each and the body is supported by props, which is optional. This practice uses Chinese meridians and helps release tension in the fascia.

Restorative Yoga

This is like Yin Yoga; however, all poses are on your back, supported by props, and held for ten to fifteen minutes each.

Yoga Nidra

This is like a guided nap. This practice is done while laying on your back and the teacher leads students through a guided relaxation to a hypnotic-like state. It is said that ninety minutes of Nidra is the equivalent of six hours of sleep!

Rock Yoga

This is my style.

Rocked and created by The Rock Yogi, Rock Yoga combines Rock and Roll, and other feel-good, empowering music with Yoga Asanas. After all, life is all about balance. With poses I've called 'The Rock Dragon', 'Rocking Chair' and 'Guitar Warrior'. I've introduced many people to the practice of Yoga with this new style, and all I hear is about how great people feel afterward. People tend to feel less intimidated in the class because they get caught up in the music, which we all know and love. Music changes us and we subconsciously and consciously respond to it.

My transition to becoming a Yoga teacher seemed like a natural one, and the timing of it all couldn't have been more perfect. While in training, I adopted my sense of style within the practice of Yoga. After bringing physical rocks and Rock and Roll into my practice with music and style, I was named "The Rock Yogi". I'm not only all 'soft and flowy' like a typical Yoga practice would be, but also another grittier, 'harder' akin to all of us Rockin' Strong badasses who just need to let some shit go!

This is not an extensive list of Yoga styles, but TRY a few and see what you like!

Now, I've come to lean on my mat as a source of release, or "taking out the garbage." Think of emotions as energy in motion, if you don't let them move, they just pile up like stinky fermenting garbage. You know the longer you leave that dirty bag there, it will continue to putrefy, and eventually make that entire room stink. If you then still don't take out that bag of garbage, it will eventually stink up the whole house and make it inhabitable. That, my friend, is the start of dis-ease. Issues are stored in your tissues. Your body is storing all these stinky negative emotions inside and they are rotting you from the inside out. You grow miserable, get aches and pains, have trouble sleeping, have less patience, etc. This makes sense because your body is storing and harbouring all this crap. Let it out. Let your emotions move through you. This is where the magic of the mind and body connection happens. You learn to breathe better through Yoga, and you can breathe into those tight restrictions within your body. That knot in your neck is stress and an emotion that is trapped. Releasing it through

Yoga movements and breath allows space and energy to replace that knot. You can now breathe deeper into your body and into the elements that make YOU.

You can find tons of scientific evidence online showing many reasons to do Yoga. Top physical benefits of Yoga Asanas include increased muscle tone and strength, improved flexibility and balance, minimized back pain, and better joint and heart health. Evidence has proven that there are health benefits to mediation as well. Studies have found perks like pain reduction, lower blood pressure, decreased risks of depression and anxiety, better breathing, mental calmness, reduced stress, and improved cognitive performance and focus. The practice of Yoga is shown to also create better self-confidence because you are more in tune with who you truly are.

I hear a lot of responses like what I had thought *"It's too slow"*, *"It's just stretching"*, or often *"Isn't Yoga just for women?"* No, no, and NO!

I've always encouraged people to TRY. It's convenient that The Rock Yogi reads as T.R.Y. In the words of Yoda, Don't T.R.Y, DO! I say DO TRY! T.R.Y. something different. What's stopping you?

Action Step:

What resonated with you? The Sunday mantras, yoga, meditations we did together made a big impact on my life and continues to do so.

Chakras and Crystal Healing

"Speak your mind, even though your voice shakes."

~ Maggie Kuhn

The Beginning – Where it Made an Impact on My Life

The day started with a text from my friend, Elise, saying that I should join an online yoga class that happened to be taking place at the current moment in her group. I went in and caught it right at the beginning. I quickly realized that I needed to start doing more yoga and adding this type of movement into my life. I'm tighter than I thought in a few places and yoga is helping me move and stretch them all out, which makes it feel better. When I was finished, I remember writing down a note about chakras, because I do make a lot of lists. I wanted to listen to Elise's throat chakra activation lesson so I typed it in, found it, and started to listen. I started picturing a spiralling blue flame moving around inside my throat– throat chakra is blue– and what I discovered that day was that, when I picture light moving in a slow spiral, it helps me visualize with great intention. I can focus on the light moving and growing more intensely. This could be a trick for those of us who have an overactive busy mind. We reached a point where she started doing the prayer to answer all prayers, the Kundalini mantra, which I had heard recently and already knew the words to! I started to say the words with her in unison, which made it even more powerful. I began to sob. I was letting so many emotions out. It was like something had taken over my body. I ended up crying three times during this meditation and, in the end, I started to picture the blue spiral flame growing inside my throat up and out. I pictured blue coming out of my mouth like music notes with every word that I spoke. All my life, I felt there was something inside me keeping me from speaking up while keeping me invisible and from being hurt along with keeping my voice quiet and unheard. A huge love feeling over took me and was bursting out of my chest. I finally started to see that now was my time to step into my voice and my own power.

What are they? The Magnificent 7

In Sanskrit, the word "chakra" means "disk" or "wheel" and refers to the spinning energy centres in your body. Physically, they are collections of nerve ganglia, and each corresponds to certain nerve bundles and major organs within the body. In Hindu or Buddhist traditions, they believe that it is within the chakras that the body and spirit come together.

To function at their best, your chakras need to stay open, or balanced, and spinning at a similar speed. Emotional ailments or physical injury can cause your chakras to spin too slowly or underactive, too quickly or overactive, and even become blocked. Sometimes, they are things we've carried from our past and can be triggered in certain circumstances. In these cases, you may experience physical or emotional symptoms related to a particular chakra.

There are hundreds of chakras within the body, 114 possible ones, but seven main chakras run from the root of your spine to the crown of your head, known as the Shushumna Nadi. These seven main chakras act as spinning gears that distribute energy to the rest throughout the body.

Crystals

I wanted to mention crystals before heading into the Chakras as they will be mentioned with each one. As with anything, crystals carry different frequencies. When placed on the Chakra location, they help strengthen this chakra. You can also hold onto the crystal while balancing your chakra or wear jewelry that contains those crystals. As you read on, this is something you may want to add to your chakra balancing. See which crystals resonate with you. If you have a strong resistance to a certain crystal, it could mean that the corresponding chakra is blocked.

Seven Main Chakras

Root Chakra

Located at the base of the spine, this chakra is red and represents our connection to the physical world and has to do with our Right to Exist. It is the foundation for all emotional and mental health and has to do with our primal connection to tribes, families, and beliefs that shape our identity. If you are blocked here, you may experience depression, anxiety, poor focus and discipline, poor boundaries, nightmares and have a lot of fear. It is the feeling of always living in "Fight or Flight." Physically, you may struggle with weight issues, hemorrhoids, constipation, or an auto-immune disease. When the root chakra is balanced, you feel confident, safe, and secure. You have a sense of trust and grounding in the world, and your parasympathetic nervous system can shift to "Rest and Digest."

How to Unblock the Root Chakra

Keep in mind that, when doing anything with Chakras, it is important to start at the root. Then everything you perform afterward will be that much more grounded and stronger.

Do anything that makes you feel like home and a sense of connection.
Examples:
- Go barefoot in nature, feel the grass between your toes, and ground to the earth.
- Have a cup of tea
- Have a wholesome diet
- Use positive visualizations
- Meditate
- Recite positive affirmations such as "I am worthy"
- Wear more red clothing
- Use a yoga balancing pose such as the Tree Pose

Crystals to Strengthen Root Chakra
- Red Jasper – a stone of empowerment
- Black Tourmaline – one of the best stones for energetic clearing, also known as the stone of protection.
- Hematite – helps you feel stable, secure, and centred. This is a great stone for anti-nausea too!

Sacral Chakra

This chakra is located at the lower belly and inner pelvis and is represented by the colour orange. It is associated with sexuality and creativity. When balanced, we can feel as if the world and ourselves are working in harmony. Our relationships with ourselves will flow easily and we can express our emotions to others with ease. We will be able to set healthy boundaries with other people. If blocked, you may feel overwhelmed, having no control, and experience erratic emotions. You might even suffer from chronic low back pain, ovarian cysts, increased allergies, bladder or kidney problems, intimacy problems, or other lower abdominal issues.

How to Unblock the Sacral Chakra

Find ways to boost your self-esteem and healthier ways of balancing your emotions
Examples:
- Eat more oranges and wear orange clothing
- Do visualization meditations
- Incorporate deep breathing exercises
- Recite positive affirmations such as "I am confident and what I offer the world is enough"
- Use hip openers in yoga such as bridge pose

Crystals to Strengthen Sacral Chakra
- Carnelian – provides courage and positivity
- Amber – can help draw dis-ease from the body, mind, and spirit and turn negative energies into positive ones.
- Peach Moonstone – soothing, calming, can help identify stored emotions in our subconscious mind

Solar Plexus Chakra

Located at the upper belly and is represented by the colour yellow, it is known for our power, self-confidence, purpose, willpower, and personality. It governs our digestive system and our gut emotional brain health. If blocked, you may experience emotional issues, insecurity, or a tendency to procrastinate. You can even experience digestive complaints such as acid reflux, ulcers, or heartburn. To align this chakra, yoga or positive affirmations work well. Try using "I am enough," "I am confident," or "I am powerful."

How to Unblock the Solar Plexus Chakra
Examples:
- Recite positive affirmations for personal power such as "I can"
- Exercise
- Recite affirmations such as "I am strong"
- Use strengthening poses such as the boat pose, warrior, or triangle
- Meditate with breathing exercises
- Wear yellow clothing

Crystals to Strengthen Solar Plexus
- Citrine –yellow quartz for healing and confidence, known for a great stone to manifest in business
- Tiger's Eye – brown and yellow are known to boost confidence, reduce fears and anxieties
- Yellow Tourmaline – can clear negative energies

Heart Chakra

Located at the center of the spine below where your heart is located, this chakra is represented by the colour green. It is known for our feelings of love, compassion, healing, and forgiveness. It is associated with our Thymus, which regulates our immune system. When aligned, we will feel joy, compassion for others, and compassion towards ourselves and our bodies. If blocked, you could feel bottled up emotions, shyness, and like you can't forgive anyone or move on. You may even tend to hold grudges more easily. Physically, we may experience cardiac issues, high or low blood pressure, issues with our lungs, and even feel lonely. The best way to unblock this chakra is to practice more gratitude, be thankful for what you do have, and even make a list of things you appreciate in your life.

How to Unblock the Heart Chakra
Examples:
- Practice gratitude
- Drink a cup of herbal tea
- Wear green clothing
- Burn some incense of lavender, rose, or orange
- Recite affirmations of love such as "I am open to love"
- Recite love mantras "om mani padme hum"
- Use heart openers such as camel pose or the wheel in yoga

Crystals to Strengthen Heart Chakra
- Green Aventurine – for good luck and abundance
- Rose Quartz – a stone of love and compassion and is one of my favourites
- Pink Calcite – a stone of forgiveness and compassion towards others

Throat Chakra

Located at the throat and represented by the colours Blue/Turquoise, it is known to be about communication, courage, and self-expression. I had a hard time keeping this chakra open myself as it can sometimes be challenging to express how you feel inside. If this chakra is blocked, you may lose creativity and feel anxiety about speaking up and lose your voice. Physical symptoms could be issues with your teeth, ears, or sinuses. You may also have a chronic sore throat or a raspy throat. I use to get that feeling when doing public speaking. I would always be clearing my throat because it felt like my airway was collapsing on me.

How to Unblock the Throat Chakra
Examples:
- Wear blue clothing
- Use Reiki which is a healing modality
- Journal your feelings
- Do neck stretches
- Use communication openers such as the Plow or Fish
- Recite positive affirmations such as "My voice is necessary", "I hear and speak the truth", "I express myself with clear intent"

Crystals to Strengthen Throat Chakra
- Aquamarine – calming, soothing, inspires trust and letting go
- Turquoise – represents good fortune and HOPE
- Blue Topaz – a crystal of joy, honesty, having manifestation properties

Third Eye Chakra

This chakra is in the center of your brow and is represented by the colour Dark Blue, Purple, or Indigo. It is strongly connected to our spirituality, our Pineal Gland, and our awareness. Your gut feeling and intuitions are connected to this chakra. If you are blocked in this chakra, you may find it hard to concentrate and hard to believe in your purpose. You may have trouble making decisions or focusing. Physically, you might have trouble sleeping, have eye discomfort, or headaches.

How to Unblock the Third Eye Chakra
Examples:
- Use purple healing crystals, wear more purple and eat more purple foods
- In yoga, connect your upper body with your lower body such as Forward Fold or Folded Eagle
- Eat dark chocolate which can put you in a better mood
- Recite positive affirmations such as "I am intuitive and I know what is good for me"
- Use a drop of essentials oil, such as Frankincense or Sandalwood, on this chakra location

Crystals to Strengthen Third Eye Chakra
- Sodalite – enhances self-esteem, calmness to the mind and can calm panic attacks
- Tanzanite – boosts the immune system, faster recovery after an illness and detoxifies and regenerates cells and tissues
- Blue Apatite – a powerful stone for manifestation, good for joints and headaches

227

Crown Chakra

The seventh chakra sits at the crown of our head is our Crown chakra, which is represented by the colours White or Violet. It is connected to our spirituality and our highest selves. As you have moved through this book, your vibrations will be raised and this will make your Crown chakra connection even stronger. If you are blocked here, you could feel lost, isolated like you can't trust the Universe. Physical ailments could be headaches, fatigue, or depression. When you are unblocked, you will experience more gratitude and joy for life.

How to Unblock the Crown Chakra
Examples:
- Recite positive affirmations such as "I feel connected to my higher self"
- Use higher Self yoga poses such as Savasana or Corpse Pose
- Do breathing exercises
- Use a gratitude practice
- Meditate

Crystals to Strengthen Crown Chakra
- Clear Quartz – known for being an amplifier for other crystals, a master healer, can boost your immune system and body
- Amethyst – a powerful stone, promotes serenity, the immune system, hormone health and can help block EMF frequencies
- Selenite – can clear other crystals by tapping them with this stone, reverse the effects of "free radicals" (the bad guys that can cause cancer), and is known for its calming abilities and bringing deep peace

Visualization

When I lived in Ontario, I went to see a Mayan Abdominal Massage woman named Nancy. As soon as I walked in, she knew one of my chakras, usually my throat, was blocked. After my massage, I would stay laying down and she would place some crystals on me and start to align them again. I would visualize the chakra sphere above its location on my body and picture the ball of energy rotating. Sometimes it would be difficult; however, I would be able to get it to start spinning. Once everything was moving again and "in balance," I would leave there feeling much better than when I first went in. This technique worked well for me. Give it a try for yourself or find someone who can help you get your chakras aligned.

As mentioned earlier, we don't want our chakras to spin too fast or too slowly. When a chakra spins in the right direction, the energy comes from us and surrounds us. The opposite direction would be taking energy from others. So, we are either pulling energy in or releasing it. If we are pulling too much negative energy in and we become out of alignment, this can lead to dis-ease within our body, which we don't want. Then, we would need to become aligned with our chakras again.

Keep in mind, this isn't a one-and-done situation. Let's face it- things happen in our lives! If you feel out of sorts or are dealing with an illness, it might be time to see about balancing your chakras.

This is a good place for me to share the directions that the chakras do spin. There are a lot of articles out there that mention that the chakras all spin clockwise; however, coming from a chakra healer, they don't all spin in the same direction and it depends on if you are female or male. For males, the first root chakra would turn clockwise, and counterclockwise for females. Moving up the chakras, each one would move in the opposite direction than the one before it, ending at the seventh crown chakra.

Gas Discharge Visualization (GDV) or Electro Photonic Imaging Camera (EPI)

I am going to briefly mention here that there are machines out there that can show you where your chakras are "out of" or "in" alignment. This was created by Dr. Konstantin Korotkov. It is a visual image of your chakras after placing your fingers into a non-invasive device for approximately thirty minutes. I had this done a few years ago and my chakras were out of alignment. You can continue onward with healing modalities to adjust your chakras or get them adjusted into alignment. Use your judgment and see if there is someone near you that could perform this analysis for you.

Action Step:

What is your experience with chakras? Have you heard of them before? Is it something that you would like to learn more about? Based on your feelings, which chakra do you think you might need to strengthen?

Visualization = Manifestation –
Time to Create Your Incredible Future

"You never know how strong you are, until you WANT to be. You better start believing it! Because it is your turn! It all starts with YOU!"

~ Tanya West

Now that you know how to empty your dustpan and get your mindset prepped for only good vibes, are you ready to create your new, incredibly amazing, fantabulous future? Did I use enough explicative words there? The future you can't wait to get to? Let's get excited here! The future where you wake up every morning and go to bed every night with a smile on your face, knowing that this will happen for you? It is up to YOU!

I have this picture hanging on my wall that I purchased right before going into the hospital:

Manifest

To remove obstacles from my life
I must understand that doubt is my only limitation
To clear the path to a new beginning
I must believe in myself
Possibilities are endless

You must remove all and any DOUBT. If you have any doubt in your mind that you can't do something, chances are you probably won't be able to do it. If you believe 100% Body, Mind, and Spirit that it is possible for you, then that is a whole new thing entirely and something very POWERFUL is going to happen. Remember, we discussed mindset at the very beginning. Let me share with you some manifestations that have happened since I started writing this book:

- Finding the exact Wonder Woman glass for sale the same day I saw it on my Instagram account.
- Winning an Amazon gift card, knowing ahead of time that it would happen.
- Looking for a cancer survivors' podcast and then, a few days later, being connected with someone who not only wrote their book about her cancer story, but also has a podcast for cancer survivors.
- Having Ireland on my digital vision board for about a year now and being connected with someone who is organizing a trip to Ireland in 2022.
- Not being able to find an editor that matched my vibe until an editor popped up at perfect timing.
- Wanting a divider to have behind me when on Zoom. One was available and it was too much. I thought to myself, "*that would be great if it was a lower price.*" Sure enough, the next day someone posted one for a fraction of the price.
- Writing about a meal I loved growing up that I would always go to my parents' house to enjoy and then suddenly, my brother ordered this meal for his birthday. My eyes lit up like it was Christmas!

- Needing some extra income and then being gifted some crystals and an EMF pendant which helped me do exactly that.

Manifestation is Magical!

(Picture sparkling twinkling stars around those words)

When I was in the hospital waiting to be sent home, someone mentioned the name Joe Dispenza to me. I started listening to a few videos about Joe and the work that he was doing. He shared with the audience that miracles were happening during his meditation sessions and even mentioned someone healing from Glioblastoma. Now, this got my interest piqued! I began to watch more of his workshops and meditations. He uses the theory that anything is possible in the Quantum Field. If you can take your mind to a place where you are no one and nobody, sitting in blackness, your intentions can become your new reality. Healing does happen here and has happened here. It can be challenging to hold a thought of nothing. I can tell you though, the more you do it, the easier it gets. It isn't always about thinking of nothing either. **It is also noticing when you AREN'T thinking about nothing.** You are the creator of your future. We don't have to wait a long time, trying to move from one matter to another matter. For example, when we say, "One day, x will happen," know that whatever you desire can happen for you now. You are the creator of your own story. You can create a new you. The science behind this theory is incredible. I highly recommend checking his research out.

For me, I focused my sessions on healing my body and being cancer-free in 2021 and onward. Letting cancer go from my body, I learned so much and found it so coincidental that suddenly, all the people I have been working with are all talking about energy chakras and how we can create our energy and radiate it out of ourselves. Activating and aligning my chakras is what I was working on already. I decided I wanted to manifest a money opportunity for me. Instead of having to try to figure everything out and create it myself, waiting for it to happen someday, it would be the right fit for me and, hey, a new couch would be great! Sending those good vibes out into the Universe and then seeing it happen, the opportunity did come to me. This is how manifestation takes place. Set your thoughts, visualize them, feel them, and let them go. Let them be.

During his workshops, these were my intentions and emotions I wanted to elevate:

Intentions:

- To be cancer-free 2021 and onward
- To INSPIRE others with my story
- To work from anywhere in the world
- To have new money opportunities flow effortlessly to me
- To have a long-term, real love relationship
- To sleep well with no meds
- To enjoy a new comfy couch

Elevated emotions:

- Joy
- Happiness
- Gratitude
- Freedom
- Confidence
- Trust

Coincidentally, I pulled an oracle card that day letting me know I had the power to manifest anything I wanted. This is exactly what I've been doing. Did I say already – no coincidences!

My Dreams:

- To always be in abundance with money and love in my life.
- To have a dream business that practically runs itself.
- To be able to share My Story of Survival and how I tapped into the Mind-Body Connection.
- To have someone that handles my social media for me and I'm living a stress-free life.
- To be living somewhere warm with my husband, and have a beautiful view every day.
- To travel the world
- To have a hypoallergenic dog that keeps us busy and fills our hearts with extra cuddles.
- To have family and friends visit often as we are within driving distance most of the year.
- To enjoy a great life and be thankful every single day.

Remember this is a feeling of your future that you create in your mind that makes you smile. Your mind doesn't know the difference between real or imagined. **YOU can create your future.** It has gotten to the point where I'm able to manifest things easily. A lot of it has to do with gratitude and being thankful for, even $10. Let the Universe know that you are thankful for all the good things that come your way and you would be surprised at how much more abundance will come to you. It got to the point where I would visualize my successful future. It was a part of my healing journey. I would picture myself on stage talking to an audience about my Survival Story, right down to the outfit I was wearing, my brand colours, and selling my book and programs on the side of the room. I would visualize this moment repeatedly and it would always make me smile inside. I could feel how it would feel inside being up there, being able to inspire hope for so many people and sharing the techniques and tools that worked for me, so they knew what was possible for them. Most days, I feel this pull towards my future and I can't wait to get there. This feeling inside me that makes me smile is the feeling of JOY. Remember, you are the one that creates this feeling in your life. It is within you, and it is the little things that make you smile no matter what your situation is. There's always something to be thankful for in your life. There's always going to be that feeling inside you that fills your heart with overwhelming joy.

Action Step:

Make a list of your intentions and the elevated emotions that will bring your vibrations up to meet those intentions. Also, create a list of your dreams you would like to experience. When you do your meditation, this is what I want you to think about. Visualize it, see it, and feel it TODAY.

Conclusion... Or Is It the Beginning of a New You?

"Though no one can go back and make a brand-new start, anyone can start from now and make a brand new ending."

~ Carl Bard

I hope you've taken value away from all the topics discussed in this book. Even if only one thing resonated with you that will help you in your healing journey, then that would make me smile. Remember that everything is a choice. We all can choose or choose not to do anything in our lives. Everything you've chosen to do has brought you to where you are today. Now you can move forward in a new direction. The choice is ultimately yours. Choose one thing, ten things, or everything. **You have the POWER to change your own life starting today. Do what works for YOU.** Always know that this is just the tip of the iceberg as there are so many more holistic practitioners that are out there and are willing to support you in your own healing experience.

As I look back through all the topics that are in this book and all the amazing people that contributed to it, I can hardly believe how much I have done. Please understand that you do not have to do everything all at once. It took me several months to accomplish all these things! It does take time. Go at your own pace, do what feels right for you, and nothing else matters. Trust yourself, forgive yourself, and start to create the amazing life that is waiting for you.

My whiteboard is my daily reminder to:

Smile
Forgive Yourself
Have FUN!
Love Yourself
Love Others
Spread JOY!

Life will throw us some curveballs and it's up to us to choose what we do with them. I do know that what I have learned is that the body-mind connection is very strong and very powerful. Waking up each morning with a smile on your face, listening to a meditation that makes you smile, going to bed at night visualizing your future in detail, and seeing exactly what you can manifest is such an incredible feeling. I cannot wait to hear about what you CAN do! It is possible! Keep me posted.

Also, remember to take some days to give yourself a break. Some days you may not feel like doing anything and that is okay, too. If you need to, cry and let it out because let's face it- it can be hard sometimes. I promise you though that, if you keep up with working at yourself regularly, things will start to get easier. I tell myself every day that I'm getting stronger and stronger in every way. My cells are full of vitality and I'm healing myself in every way, every day. I am safe, I've got this.

The key here is, **YOU have to believe it**.

Thank you to everyone who contributed to this book. I truly appreciate how much you have supported me, and I will be forever grateful for everything that you have done for me. This book is filled with inspiration for whatever your journey will be. Wishing you all the best in life. I know you can do this too.

Going through this incredible journey has made me realize that at this point in my life:

I'm happier than I've ever been.
My relationships with my friends are stronger than ever.
I'm healthier than I've ever been in my entire life!
Mentally, spiritually, and physically!
I am in LOVE with my life.

Looking back to the moment when I was putting all the pieces together to create this book, I remember thinking to myself, "Wow! I have such incredibly amazingly talented friends!" It made me get very emotional- happy tears this time. These are the people to whom I will be forever grateful every single day of my life.

Thank you for being a part of my healing journey.

When I first got out of the hospital, I wrote this down.

I will inspire and make a difference in the world.
I will make people's lives better.
Be the reason they smile, because I was able to gift them
something that impacted their life in a big way.
I will find a way to make this happen.
Spreading joy and kindness lights me up.
I CAN do this!

I hope that I have.

With love,
Tanya

Bonus Tips

Life Insurance and Critical Illness

One thing I am very thankful for is that I did get life insurance in my twenties, even though I had no children at the time, I do feel this was a smart move. Only a few years later, I developed cancer and my rates would have gone up drastically, and I wondered if anyone would have even insured me after that diagnosis. For those of you who do not have life insurance, I would suggest contacting your insurance provider and at least getting a quote so you know how much you would be paying each month for life insurance. You just never know what can happen in life and I'm so thankful that I do have life insurance already in place.

Also, as a self-employed person, I had the opportunity to purchase critical illness insurance. This was something that I had considered but seeing as I was already signing up for life insurance, I didn't think that I could afford an additional amount each month for a critical illness policy. I do truly regret this decision. When I received my cancer diagnosis only a few years later, I would have received $100,000. This would have changed my life at the time. Even now, I know a lot of people who do not know about critical illness for self-employed individuals. It isn't that expensive, and I would highly suggest that, if you are self-employed, you contact your insurance provider or a financial advisor and find out more information about this opportunity. Even a simple quote won't cost you anything but your time.

Financial Gifts

When I went into the hospital for my brain surgery, it was last minute and was considered emergency brain surgery. I was self-employed and, at the time, I didn't know what I would do financially after the surgery. I am so thankful that a GoFundMe was set up while I was in the hospital. Through the kindness of my community, they were able to raise money even while in the hospital and that made a difference in my life moving forward. After talking with my bookkeeper, getting some advice from you, I made notes of the donations that people give you that are financial amounts. Mark them down as gifts, you don't need to pay tax on these in Alberta. Check with your bookkeeper.

Squatty Potty

I wish I had been told about The Squatty Potty a lot sooner or should have gone out and purchased something that would help me in the bathroom. If you're someone dealing with constipation or hemorrhoids, this is something that you want to give a try. Try not to strain or hurt yourself. That was what I learned the first time around after being constipated for seven days after each chemo- brick city. Even if you buy a dollar store step stool, it'll be worth it. Our bodies were designed to have our legs crouched for proper elimination. Trust me... again, you'll thank me for this later.

P.S. Always flush with the toilet seat down or that shit will get everywhere!

Dry Brushing

I would dry brush my skin a few times a week before taking a shower. This increased my circulation, got my blood flowing, and removed any dead skin cells before taking a shower. It feels good to do this. Always remember to move in circular motions towards your heart and don't press too hard. This experience should not be painful in any way.

If you don't already have a dry skin brush, see the resources section for a recommendation or go to your local health store. Typically, they would have one in stock.

Thermography

When I was a business consultant, a former client of mine started a thermography business. For those of you not familiar with thermography, it's a thermal image of the hot spots inside your body. Cancer generates a lot of heat, and it may be possible to detect cancer long before a mammography scan would have. It is also possible to have your entire body scanned through this thermal imaging procedure.

I ended up having two scans done over the years and the cost is roughly $250 per scan. Some insurance benefit packages will cover parts of the scan. Ask your insurance provider about the details on this. Do your research and ask lots of questions. You are looking for a clinic that performs a cold challenge. This is where you place your hands in cold water before the scan. To ensure you are getting a more accurate reading.

The Dentist and Mercury Fillings

Do you agree or not agree with having mercury fillings removed from your mouth? I had mine removed many years ago as I felt it wasn't a good thing to have in my body. Just like we want to avoid getting any mercury from fish, we don't want mercury in our mouth either! If you feel the same way, do your research and find a holistic dentist that has done this before, and knows the proper procedures for removing mercury amalgams from your mouth. It must be done correctly so your body does not absorb the fumes from having the mercury removed. I've never regretted having them removed and filled with non-toxic white fillings. You decide for yourself. Over the years, I've read too many stories of how people's health has improved after having mercury amalgams removed from their mouth. The choice is ultimately yours!

Action Step:

Do you have any mercury fillings in your mouth? Write down your thoughts on this topic, do your research and decide for yourself.

Resources Available

Wellspring Programs

Reach out to the resources around you that could help you with your current health situation. I've contacted Wellspring Programs when I lived in Ontario and again when I lived in Edmonton. They offer lots of free programs that you can use in your healing Journey. Give them a call or go online and see what they have available. So far, I have used the Reiki sessions during radiation, during chemotherapy, and even when I go in for an MRI. A simple phone call lets them know when to provide this healing modality for you. I've also done some fun stuff like a Zentangle class, which did help me clear my mind and focus on something fun for a while. There are cooking classes too! Check them out and see what they might have at this point that can help you as well?

"Wellspring is the only organization in Canada that provides supportive care for Canadians with all cancers, at all stages, and in all communities across the country. No other organization does what we do.

Wellspring is not about cancer. We are about helping those with cancer, their caregivers, and family members manage everything in their lives that change because of cancer.

And we provide all our programs and services at absolutely no charge." ~ Wellspring.ca

Action Step:

Make a list of who you can reach out to. There may be a Wellspring near you or something similar. During COVID, many of the courses were virtual which was great!

"Always remember you are BRAVER than you think, STRONGER than you seem, and LOVED MORE than you know!"

~ Unknown

Outtakes – AKA Hilarious Moments

Moment #1

When in the hospital, I realized that my eyes were worse than they were before surgery, and I was just waiting for them to heal or line up. I even asked for an eye patch – seriously – so I could read better. I'd ask people in the hospital to write in all caps when they were sending me messages so I could read their messages easier. When I got home and I was saying how I was having a hard time reading, my friend reminded me that I used to wear glasses to read. We both looked at each other and laughed about that for hours!

Moment #2

When getting tested for the Alberta Cancer Exercise or ACE study program, I was asked to do a plank at the very end. The medication I was currently on after just being out of the hospital made me very burpy and anyone who knows me knows I have not burped much in my life. Don't ask me why. I would get these little gurgles that would just make noise, yet never really come out. This gas would build up inside me to the point of extreme uncomfortableness.

Attempting to do the plank aggravated this feeling and I rushed to the bathroom to self-burp to get the gas out. I opened the door from the bathroom to find my friend Keomi and the guy from the ACE Program right outside the door asking if everything was okay. I was embarrassed and thankful that my friend Keomi had shown me how to self-burp only a few weeks before this day. Picture me over the bathtub, patting on my chest as the burps came up and out. Otherwise, it could have been a disaster. Every time I meet with the guy from the ACE study program for a review, he always reminds me of the plank incident. I will forever be known as the girl who got sick while trying to do a plank. Then again, I'm probably not the first one!

Moment #3

On May 5th, 2021, I combed my hair for the first time in five months, which was a real celebration, except for one bald spot. Later that day, I was vacuuming and decided to empty my vacuum. Well, I found out where all the hair went! Ewwww!

Moment #4

Read the labels on your supplements carefully. You wouldn't want to take them incorrectly! I would never do that. Okay, I might have...once...okay, twice.

"Out of your vulnerabilities will come your strength."

~ Sigmund Freud

Author Connections

Join me online for more holistic healing tips that will change your future.

Our Group:
www.facebook.com/groups/strongerthanyourealize
Instagram:
www.instagram.com/gowithwest
Resource List of Products Mentioned -
www.tanyawest.ca/bookresources

Tanya West
www.tanyawest.ca

Rae-ann Wood-Schatz
Integrity Seminars
www.integrityseminars.com
www.raeannwoodschatz.com
In Person or Virtual Services

Jesse Wood-Schatz
Medicine Valley Farms
www.medicinevalleyfarms.com
In Person Services

Karen Quinlan
Karen's Pure Balance
www.karenspurebalance.com
Virtual Services

Christina Vignal
Connect in Wellness
massagethatrocks@hotmail.com
In Person Services

Corby Furrow
Transformational Catalyst
Radiant Core Solutions
www.radiantcoresolutions.com
discover@radiantcoresolutions.com
In Person or Virtual Services

Certification Level Training
National Emotional Freedom Techniques Training
Institute (NeftTi)
www.neftti.com
Corby@neftti.com
Virtual Services

Elise Brathwaite
www.elisebrathwaite.com
elise@elisebrathwaite.com
In Person or Virtual Services

Danielle Beaulieu
The Rock Yogi
Instagram @the_rock_yogi
In Person or Virtual Services

References

My Cancer Story: Where This Journey Began

I am Stronger Than You Realize - Journal
https://www.tanyawest.ca

Food and Supplements

https://www.ewg.org/foodnews/summary.php

For the Love of Tea

https://www.medicalnewstoday.com/articles/323648

Microgreens & Medicine Valley Farms

Binder, Graham. "Mighty Microgreens." *Mighty Microgreens | College of Agriculture & Natural Resources, University of Maryland*, 6 Sept. 2012, agnr.umd.edu/news/ mighty microgreens.

Canada, Health. "Government of Canada." *Canada.ca*, / Government Du Canada, 29 Nov. 2010, www.canada.ca/en/ health-canada/services/food-nutrition/healthy-eating/

dietary-reference-intakes/tables/reference-values-vitamins-dietary-reference-intakes-tables-2005.html.

Coyle, Daisy. "Sulforaphane: Benefits, Side Effects, and Food Sources." *Healthline*, Healthline Media, 26 Feb. 2019, www.healthline.com/nutrition/sulforaphane.

Koon, Robin. "Carotenoids: From (Vitamin) A to Zeaxanthin." *Carotene*, 31 Oct. 2018, www.carotene.org/carotenoids-vitamin-zeaxanthin/.

National Center for Biotechnology Information. "PubChem Compound Summary for CID 14985, Vitamin E" *PubChem*, https://pubchem.ncbi.nlm.nih.gov/compound/Vitamin-E. Accessed 6 June 2021.

Neves, Andrew. "BROCCOLI MICROGREENS NUTRITION: EVERYTHING YOU NEED TO KNOW." *Microgreens World*, Microgreens World, 10 Apr. 2021, microgreensworld.com/broccoli-microgreens-nutrition/.

Xiao, Zhenlei, et al. "Assessment of Vitamin and Carotenoid Concentrations of Emerging Food Products: Edible Microgreens." *Journal of Agricultural and Food Chemistry*, vol. 60, no. 31, 2012, pp. 7644–7651., doi:10.1021/jf300459b.

Essential Oils

(1) Dr. Mariza Snyder Smart Mom's Guide to Essential Oils page 14
(2) https://naturallivingfamily.com/diy-essential-oil-guide-for-body-care-products/
(3) https://naturallivingfamily.com/essential-oils-for-cancer/

(4) Dr. Mariza Snyder Smart Mom's Guide to Essential Oils page 94

(5) Dr. Mariza Snyder Smart Mom's Guide to Essential Oils page 192/193

(6) Dr. Mariza Snyder Smart Mom's Guide to Essential Oils page 93/94

Move Your Body

http://www.livescience.com/54749-exercise-reducescancer-risk.html

Earthing: Soaking up Mother Nature

https://www.healthline.com/health/grounding#the-science

Acupuncture

https://www.mayoclinic.org/tests-procedures/acupuncture/about/pac-20392763

Electro Magnetic Fields and Frequencies

Stop Frying Your Brain With Your Cell Phone - https://youtu.be/4Xc9EsEdz8Y

How to Unblock the Heart Chakra

https://www.goodnet.org/articles/5-ways-to-open-your-heart-chakra
https://www.healing-art-community.com/the-seven-major-chakras/

Chakras and Crystal Healing

https://www.healing-art-community.com/the-seven-major-chakras/